SCIENCE MAGIC

Would you like to cook an egg in a glass dish held in your hands? Try using light that is also heat. Turn to page 102 to find out how.

SCIENCE MAGIC

BY

KENNETH M. SWEZEY

(Photographs by the Author)

McGRAW-HILL BOOK COMPANY, INC.

NEW YORK   LONDON   TORONTO

Library of Congress Catalog Card Number: 52-8332

Published by the McGraw-Hill Book Company, Inc.

Printed in the United States of America

FOURTEENTH PRINTING
62589

A WORD OF CAUTION

Nearly all of the experiments in this book can be performed by anyone, with common materials and without taking special precautions. A few that require laboratory chemicals and involve fire have, however, been included for the benefit of the science student and hobbyist. If the inexperienced reader wishes to perform the latter stunts he can do so safely if he follows the instructions faithfully, keeps fire away from all combustible materials, and handles acids and concentrated hydrogen peroxide just as carefully as he would household lye or the acid in his car battery.

A WORD OF EXPLANATION

Would you like to experience some magic that is *real*? Then forget for a moment the hocus-pocus of the stage magician and investigate a few of the wonders of the everyday world of science around you!

What makes jet planes fly? How do atomic particles go right through solids without making a hole? How can scientists squeeze rain from the clouds? What makes your refrigerator stay frigid? How do chemists mix colorless substances and wind up with dyes and pigments that rival the rainbow?

The purpose of *Science Magic* is to help you find the answers to these and to more than 120 other baffling questions in science and to have a good time doing so.

Like the experiments in the author's previous book, *After-dinner Science*, most of the stunts that follow can be performed with tumblers, bottles, drinking straws, and other household gadgets, and with chemicals from the kitchen or drugstore.

In some cases, the magic in the present book takes the form of amusing tricks which can be used for entertainment at the dinner table, a party, or before the science class or club. In others, it demonstrates new synthetic materials—such as silicones or fluorescent dyes —or shows you how to seed clouds, make X-ray photographs, or watch the trails of cosmic rays in your kitchen. Where possible, the magic has been adapted to practical uses. In no case is an experiment *merely* a trick; every one is backed by sound science.

The best science magic is timeless. In choosing his material, the author searched the whole field of science literature—from ancient times to the latest development in the newspapers. When an experiment was old, the author tried to adapt it for presentation with modern materials, and to point it up either with its own history or with happenings of today. Many of the new experiments he devised in his own kitchen and appear here in book form for the first time.

THANK YOU TO THESE

Many of the pictures and some of the text of *Science Magic* have appeared in *Popular Science Monthly*. The author wishes to thank the editors of that magazine both for their permission to adapt this material and for their indefatigable prodding in getting him to turn it out.

It would be impossible to express appreciation to all the individuals who helped make this book. Some of them would be the great classical experimenters; others would be completely unknown. Special thanks, however, must go to Professor Howard Nechamkin, of Pratt Institute, Brooklyn, New York, for providing the material for the plastics test table; to Dr. Vincent Schaefer of the General Electric Company for inspiring the cloud-seeding experiment (Dr. Schaefer produced the first man-made snowstorm by dropping dry ice into a cloud); to engineers of the Brookhaven National Laboratory for suggesting the peanut-butter-jar cloud chamber; and to the United States Secret Service for the material on detecting counterfeit coins.

And, of course, the author cannot forget these faithful and dear friends who helped with the experiments and posed for the pictures: Ray Albert, Howard and Ruby Balke, John and Alice Byrne, Richard Ciccarello, Donald Cluen, Richard Dempsey, Daniel D'Errico, Harry Dewdney, John Duffy, Edward and Evelyn Eckstein, Jean and Karen Eckstein, David Findlay, William Halpin, Tommy and Jane Hooker, Tommy and Margaret Killeen, Daniel Korbelak, William McGarry, and Robert Turner.

KENNETH M. SWEZEY

CONTENTS

Fluid Mechanics

Fluids in Motion

Sound and Vibration

Little Brother of Lightning

Magnets and Electric Currents

Fire and Heat

Ice, Cold, and Man-made Rain

Light—Visible and Invisible

Seeing Is Deceiving

x

SCIENCE MAGIC

When our friend on the revolving stool throws the pillow, she will be pushed backward by the reaction. Jet planes work on a similar principle.

JET PLANES, FORCES, AND POWER

How a Jet Plane Gets Its Push

What makes jet planes streak through the sky faster than sound? How can rockets propel themselves through outer space where there is no oxygen for combustion and no air to "push against"?

First of all, let's dispel the notion that jets and rockets are propelled by the stream of hot gases pushing out against the air behind them. Although a jet plane does need air to support its wings and to supply oxygen for burning its fuel, the air hinders rather than helps the forward motion of the plane. Because a rocket carries its own oxygen supply, this type of jet craft travels best where there is no air at all!

What actually speeds a jet or rocket on its way is the forward kick of the expanding gases, a kick that is equal and opposite to the kick that sends the gases backward.

Newton explained the principle in his famous third law of motion. According to this law, you can't push against anything without the thing pushing back with equal force. You can't walk, for example, unless the pavement pushes forward on your feet just as hard as your feet push backward. You can't throw a ball, either, without the ball pushing back on your hand.

If you doubt the last statement, just throw a pillow (or a ball) with all your might while seated on a revolving stool.

Does your body turn in the direction in which the pillow is thrown? Not at all. As long as your hand pushes forward against the pillow, the pillow pushes back against your hand. As a result, your body retreats as the pillow advances. The heavier the pillow, and the harder you throw it, the farther you turn backward.

In rockets and jets, the molecules of expanding gas may be likened to minute pillows being hurled rearward from the nozzle. The faster these "pillows" are thrown, and the more there are of them, the harder they push the plane in the opposite direction.

3

Reaction Makes This Turbine Spin

Do you think jet propulsion is something new? Near the beginning of the Christian Era, the Greek inventor-philosopher Heron of Alexandria described in one of his books, the *Pneumatica*, the first steam engine on record. Although this engine was scarcely more than a toy, it was jet-propelled!

Heron's primitive turbine consisted of a hollow metal globe mounted on pivots and provided with two bent outlet pipes attached on opposite sides. Steam, supplied to the globe through one of the pivots, shot out from these pipes in opposite directions. The kickback of the steam against them caused the globe to spin.

Next time you get a carton of ice cream packed in dry ice, why not use the carton and the dry ice to make a modernized working

4

model of that earliest jet-propelled machine? Everything you need is shown in the photograph on the opposite page.

Make the two nozzles from 3-inch lengths of a soda straw, fastening them with sealing wax over small holes punched in opposite sides of the container. Curve them as shown, and strengthen the "elbow" with another bit of sealing wax. After the nozzles have been installed, place the container on a small pie plate and float the plate on water in a large pan.

To operate your turbine, put about ½ inch of water in the container, drop in a small piece of dry ice (be sure to handle dry ice with tongs or a cloth), and put on the cover. Heat from the water causes the dry ice to change rapidly into carbon dioxide gas. This gas, streaming from the straws, reacts against them and causes your improvised machine to rotate merrily (as shown above).

5

Peroxide Launches a Rocket

To most of us, the term *hydrogen peroxide* conjures up visions of cut fingers and "peroxide blondes." It may come as a surprise to find out that this same chemical—concentrated to thirty times the strength of the drugstore variety—can drive submarines and torpedoes, help power jet planes, and launch rockets!

Chemically, hydrogen peroxide is just water with an extra atom of oxygen attached to each molecule. Its abilities as antiseptic, bleach, and source of power are all due to its readiness to part with this oxygen. On contact with human tissue, hair, or dyes, 3 per cent peroxide decomposes mildly, giving off 10 volumes of oxygen. Treated with a chemical catalyst, 90 per cent peroxide breaks up violently into 4,000 volumes of oxygen and steam!

During World War II, 90 per cent hydrogen peroxide helped drive the Messerschmitt 163, the first rocket plane ever to see fighting service. Sent into turbines, steam and oxygen from peroxide drove torpedoes, fast submarines, and the pumps which fed fuel into the firing chamber of the giant V-2 rocket. Explosive decomposition of peroxide in a piston-fitted launching cylinder gave the V-1 "buzz bomb" the 250-m.p.h. push it needed to get under way. Concentrated peroxide is used similarly in jets and rockets of today.

Although 90 per cent peroxide is restricted to research and military use, the 30 per cent variety is potent enough to demonstrate the expansive force of this chemical. If you can get a little 30 per cent peroxide from a chemical supply house or your school lab, you can use it to operate the miniature rocket launcher shown on the next page. (Thirty per cent peroxide is corrosive and decomposes easily. Handle it as carefully as you would lye or a strong acid!)

Construction is shown, left. The expansion chamber is a 2-ounce bottle closed with a 2-hole stopper. Fit a glass tube, 6 inches long and ⅛-inch inside diameter,

into one of the holes and leave the other open to accommodate a
medicine dropper. Carve the "rocket" from balsa wood, and push
a matchstick into it for a tail.

Cover bottom of bottle with powdered manganese dioxide, stopper bottle *lightly* (so stopper will act as a safety valve if gas pressure
gets too high), and place rocket tail in the tube. With the rocket out
of range of anyone's eyes, insert the partly filled dropper into the open
hole and squeeze out *one drop* of peroxide.

Instantly, the manganese dioxide breaks down the peroxide into
oxygen and steam. The latter send the rocket to the ceiling!

You can launch the rocket again and again before you have to
empty the bottle and recharge it with manganese dioxide.

You Can't Straighten the Cord!

Why are electric power lines festooned in easy curves between poles, instead of being pulled taut? Why must clotheslines and picture wires be allowed a certain amount of slack?

You can get a clue—and perhaps surprise yourself at the same time—by trying the stunt shown above. Tie a book to the middle of a strong cord about 4 feet long, wrap the ends of the cord around your hands for a better grip, and then try to straighten the cord. No matter how strong you are, you can't do it!

Why? Because the flatter the angle between the two halves of the cord, the more force you must apply to sustain the book. The cord would snap under force great enough to make it horizontal!

Clotheslines and picture wires must be left slack for the same reason. When nearly horizontal, either could be snapped by a comparatively light load. Power lines, if pulled too tight, could break under their own weight.

Salt Can Sometimes Be Strong

Here's a science puzzler to try on the strong man at a party. All you need is a tube of thick glass or metal about ½ inch in diameter and a foot long, a slightly longer dowel that fits the tube loosely, salt, a paper napkin, and a rubber band.

First cap one end of the tube with two thicknesses of the napkin paper, holding it in place with the rubber band. Next pour 3 inches of salt into the tube and insert the dowel. Then present the device to your victim and challenge him to force off the cap by a steady push on the dowel. Unless the salt is too loosely packed, or your friend is a superman, the cap won't budge!

The secret? The downward force exerted by the dowel is largely converted into oblique and sideways forces by the particles of salt. As a result, most of the push is sustained by the walls of the tube.

Sand effectively stops bullets, and the earth above tunnels and subways supports itself, largely for the same reason.

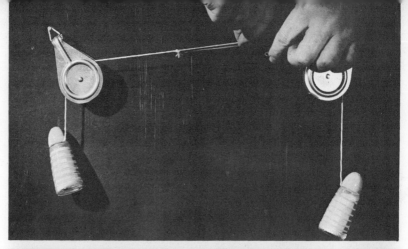

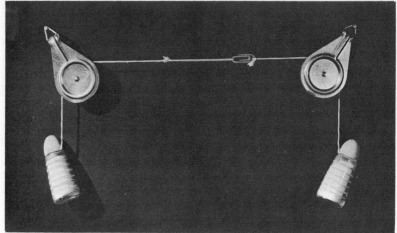

Can Two Teams Pull Harder Than One?

In a tug of war, does the pull of the second team put more strain on the rope than if one end were tied to, say, a tree?

Anyone who says "yes" is wrong, and this stunt will prove it. Hang two similar salt shakers (or other small equal weights) over two pulleys by means of cords. To the free end of one cord tie a rubber band, and to the free end of the other a paper clip.

To make your test, first hold the free end of the rubber band (top photo, above) and note its stretch under the weight of a single salt shaker. Then hook on the cord attached to the second salt shaker and note the stretch again (lower photo, above).

The stretch in each case is the same! Why? Because the second weight merely replaces the reactive pull of your hand.

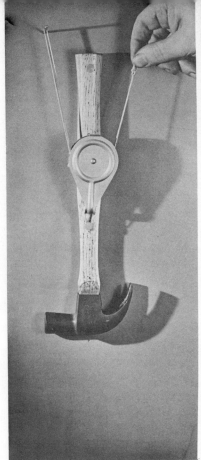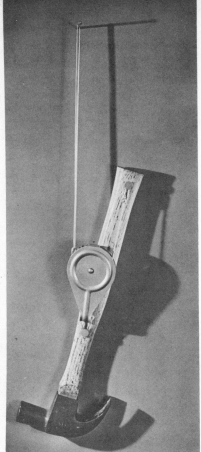

A Hammer Paradox

In the setup shown above, left, a hammer is supported by a rubber band tied to a cord, the cord passing under a pulley fastened to the hammer handle. The free end of the rubber band is hung on a nail, while you hold the free end of the cord.

The problem is this: if you hook the end of the cord over a thumbtack at the end of the hammer handle, instead of holding it, will the rubber band stretch more, less, or remain the same?

The photograph above, right, gives the surprising answer. The rubber band now stretches nearly twice as much as it did in the first case! Why? Because it is required to support the entire weight of the hammer, whereas in the first case it supported only half the weight while your hand supported the other half.

11

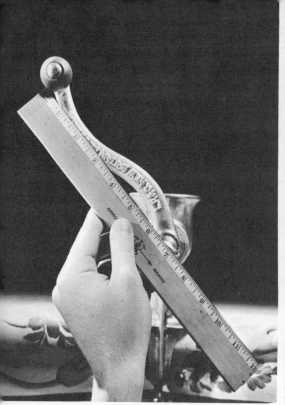

Test Your Own Horsepower

Do you think you're as strong as a horse? You can quickly find out with the aid of such everyday instruments as a watch, a ruler, a spring balance, and a meat grinder.

James Watt, Scottish inventor of the first practical steam engine, devised the term *horsepower* back in the 1780s to help show mine and mill operators how many live horses his newfangled engines could replace.

In Watt's day, horses that operated mill wheels and mine pumps trudged around in circles at the ends of long poles. Watt measured the distance a horse would walk in a minute, measured the pounds pull on the pole, and multiplied. A strong dray horse, he found, could continuously exert about 22,000 foot-pounds a minute. For good measure he added 50 per cent, and established 33,000 foot-pounds per minute as the standard horsepower for rating his engines.

You can determine your own horsepower by a domesticated ver-

12

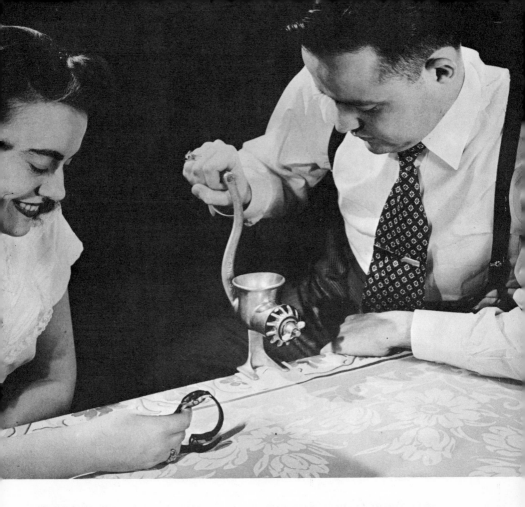

sion of Watt's method. First calculate the distance the grinder arm turns in one revolution; to do so, measure its length and multiply this figure by 6.28. Next, tighten the nut on the grinder until it requires about 20 pounds pull to turn the handle steadily. Then—while a friend counts revolutions and keeps time—turn the handle as fast as you can for exactly one minute.

To find your horsepower, multiply the circumference (in *feet*) by the pounds pull. Then multiply the resulting number .by the revolutions per minute. Finally divide by 33,000. The figure you get represents the horsepower exerted by your arm.

You are a real he-man if you develop more than $\frac{1}{10}$ horsepower by this method. In a short spurt of running upstairs, a man may develop more than 1 horsepower. Oddly enough, an average horse, performing average work, develops only $\frac{2}{3}$ horsepower!

GRAVITY AND BALANCE

Which Ruler Will Win?

There's a scientific reason for the fact that a small boy is more apt to fall all the way when he trips than is a tall man. Because the man's *center of oscillation*—the point in his body at which all his falling weight seems to be concentrated—is higher, the man must fall farther. Hence, he has more time to catch himself.

In objects of uniform cross section, or of similar proportion, the taller the object the higher will be its center of oscillation and so the longer the object will take to fall.

You can demonstrate this by staging a falling race between two rulers of different length. Stand them on end, side by side, and release both at the same instant. The shorter one will win.

That the time of fall is really determined by the height of the center of oscillation, and not by the actual height of the object, can be proved by weighting the longer ruler near the bottom and repeating the race. This time the longer one wins!

 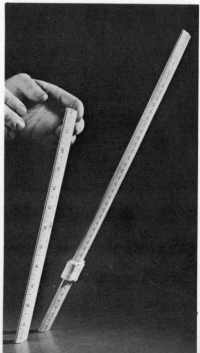

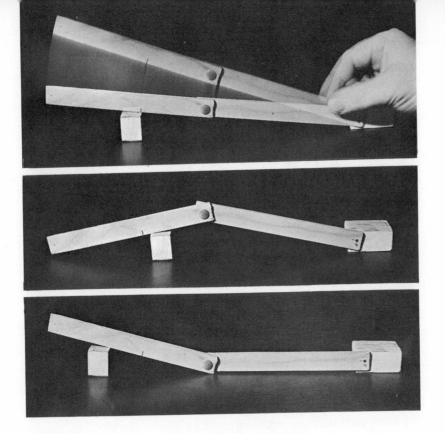

Strike Here for Best Results

Baseball players, swordsmen, and woodchoppers all know by experience the meaning of the center of oscillation. For the center of oscillation is also the *center of percussion*—the exact spot on a bat, sword, or ax which delivers the most powerful blow without transmitting vibration to the user's hands.

How the center of percussion acts can be shown by the simple stunts pictured above. Cut a thin stick in two, fasten the halves together with a thumbtack, and pivot the end of one with a small nail to a wood block. (Set the thumbtack just firmly enough to keep the outer half from dropping under its own weight.)

In a uniform stick, the center of percussion is about two-thirds the distance from the point of support. If, therefore, you let this compound stick fall so it strikes another block two-thirds of the way from the end pivot, the joint will remain perfectly straight. However, if the block is shifted inward or outward away from this point, the impact will cause it to buckle.

15

What Does Your Hydrometer Indicate?

The hydrometer that tells you when your car battery needs recharging, when your antifreeze will freeze, how much alcohol is in a drink, doesn't really determine any of these facts at all. It merely determines *specific gravity*, the weight of the solution under test compared with an equal amount of water. Luckily, this figure often gives clues to other characteristics of a solution.

You can make a working model of a hydrometer by placing a small vial, weighted with shot or sand so it will float upright, in a glass of water. If you add salt to the water the vial will rise—the more salt, the higher. This is because salt water is heavier (has a higher specific gravity) than plain water.

By placing in the vial a slip of paper marked with graduations, you can readily compare the relative densities of various fluids.

The secret of multicolored drinks in which the layers do not mix lies in choosing liquids of different densities. Although you can't drink the amazing concoction shown on the next page, you can at least display it as an unusual demonstration of specific gravity! To make it, start with a layer of mercury. (If you haven't any mercury, begin with the next layer.) On this, float an iron nut (for mercury is nearly twice as heavy as iron!). Then pour in carbon tetrachloride and float a plastic bottle cap on it. Next, pour in water and put on it a block of wood weighted with tacks. As a final flourish, add a layer of salad oil and a cork!

16

The Mysterious Bubble Dancer

Don't let the fact that gases and vapors are made of pretty thin stuff fool you into thinking they have no weight. Dirigibles float in air because the hydrogen or helium in their gas bags is lighter than the air it displaces. Balloons filled with air can, likewise, float on a gas or vapor that is heavier than air.

You can prove this with air-filled soap bubbles. Put several teaspoonfuls of carbon tetrachloride (nonflammable Carbona will do) into a deep bowl. Place the bowl in a dish of hot water and leave it undisturbed in a draft-free place for 5 or 10 minutes.

Then blow a soap bubble and drop it carefully into the dish. Instead of falling to the bottom, as it would do if nothing but air were present, the bubble will dance about mysteriously as if on an invisible cushion. The vapor of carbon tetrachloride, which is more than five times as heavy as air, buoys it up.

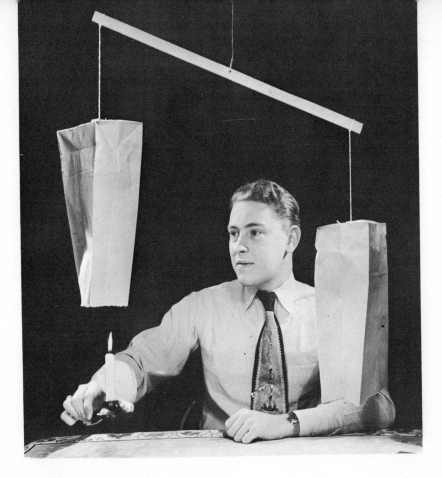

Hot Air Lifts a Balloon

The great-grandfather of the modern dirigible was a balloon sent up in France nearly two centuries ago by Joseph and Jacques Montgolfier. The Montgolfier brothers, watching clouds in the sky, had reasoned that if they could enclose some cloudlike vapor in a large and light bag, the vapor might rise and carry the bag with it. They finally proved this theory by constructing a huge linen bag, inflating it over a fire, and then setting it free. The bag rose to great height and finally landed more than a mile away.

This first practical balloon was carried aloft merely by hot air. Since air expands when it is heated, warm air is lighter than an equal volume of air at a lower temperature. For proof, suspend two paper bags upside down from an improvised balance, and hold a lighted candle at a safe distance below one of them. As the air inside heats up, the bag rises—just as did the Montgolfiers' balloon.

19

Hot Water Makes a Volcano

Hot water flows upward in a heating system because liquids (as well as gases, such as air) are lighter when expanded by heat. Transference of heat by the physical movement of liquids or gases is called *convection*, from a Latin word meaning "to carry."

By means of the simple setup shown above, you can actually *see* how convection works.

Fill a small vial about two-thirds full of hot water, and add ink to the brim to color it. Then stand this bottle, mouth open, in a large jar of cold water. Immediately a plume of hot inky water will rise and spread like a cloud from a miniature volcano. As the inky water cools, it gains density and slowly descends.

Water rises and descends through a heating plant because of similar changes in density.

How Heavy Is the Apple?

At a dinner party, a dispute arose among calorie-conscious guests as to the weight of a big beautiful apple which the host had produced and which he was wondering whether he dare eat. Guesses ranged all the way from 4 ounces to a pound. With no scale in the house, nothing could be proved until someone suggested a simple scientific trick for weighing the apple with items readily at hand. Can you guess how this was done?

A large pitcher filled to the brim with water was placed in a serving dish, and the apple was floated in the water. The water that spilled into the dish was measured in an ordinary measuring cup. As the water displaced by any floating body weighs exactly the same as the body, the 5 ounces of water that had spilled over represented the weight of the apple!

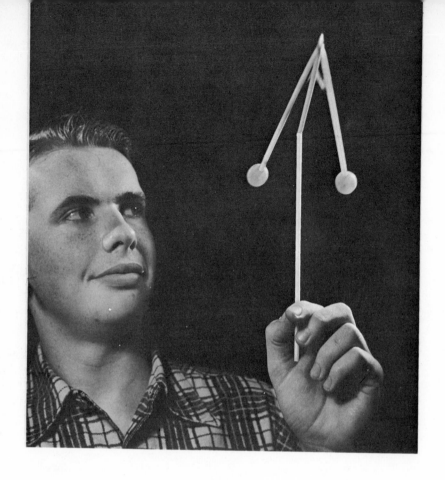

Balancing Magic

To invent incredible balancing stunts, or to duplicate old favorites, is easier than you think. Just follow this rule: keep the center of gravity of any combination of objects (the point at which its weight seems to be concentrated) *below* the point of support.

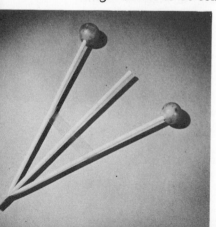

Above, for example, three drinking straws are balanced in an unreasonable position on the tip of a fourth. Grapes or olives on the ends of the two outer straws put the center of gravity of the system where it is needed.

The photograph at the left shows how to assemble the gimmick to be balanced.

22

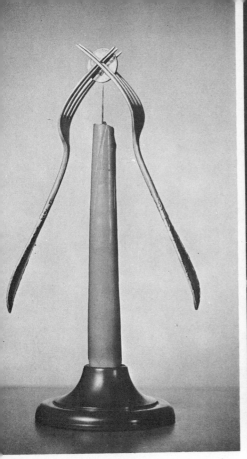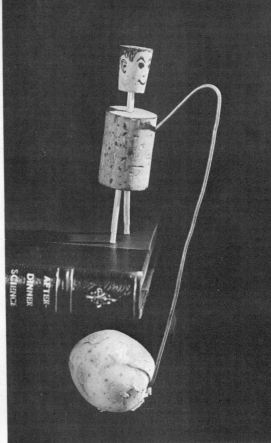

Fan out three straws, pinch their ends together where they join, and bind the joint with cellophane tape. For reinforcement, attach another piece of tape about 3 inches farther along. Push a grape or an olive on the end of each of the outer straws, and cut the center straw so that it's slightly shorter than the other two.

You should now be able to balance the resulting assemblage on the tip of another straw—with what appears to be most of its weight supported by nothing!

The stunts at the top of this page may also be put together in a jiffy. The forks and coin, balanced on the point of a needle, are so stable that they can be spun around. The match-and-cork fisherman, stabilized by a potato on the end of his "fishing line" (made of wire from a coat hanger), will rock back and forth interminably on the edge of a book or table.

A Box That Rolls Uphill

By so weighting a round candy box that its center of gravity is at the edge—instead of at the center, where is belongs—you can puzzle your unsuspecting friends by making the box roll uphill or downhill, at will!

The secret gimmick is a strip of lead, about 1 by 2 inches, cut from an old pipe. Bend this in **J** form and clamp it over the edge of the open box, with the long leg inside. When you replace the cover, mark the position of the weight.

To make the box roll downhill, place it on the incline so that the weight is near the top but slightly on the downhill side. To make it seem to defy gravity, place the box at the bottom of the incline with the weight at the top but toward the uphill side.

Make your hill short enough so that the box will roll over the top just as the weight reaches the bottom. You should, of course, surreptitiously remove the weight before letting your curious friends try the stunt.

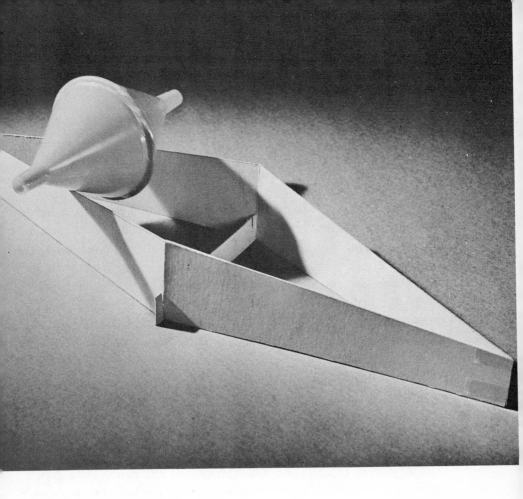

The Gravity-defying Funnels

Place a pair of joined funnels at either end of the track shown above. Seeming to defy gravity, they will roll to the middle, the highest point!

Don't believe for a moment, however, that the funnels really disobey the law of Newton. As in most scientific paradoxes, the catch lies in an incorrect interpretation of the facts. Although the funnels seem to be rolling uphill, their center of gravity is really going downhill, because of the widening track.

Any funnels having a smooth surface may be used. Join their mouths with tape. Make the cardboard track higher at the center than at the ends by an amount less than the radius of the funnels; spread the track less than the distance between their necks.

MATTER IS LAZY

Inertia Drives Nails and Cushions Blows

Applied to human beings, the term *inertia* usually suggests merely an unwillingness to "get going." Applied to matter, however, inertia means not only an unwillingness to start but also an unwillingness to *stop*, once a body is moving! You can demonstrate both of these tendencies dramatically by a pair of party stunts.

In the first (shown on the facing page), you balance 25 or 30 pounds of books on your head; then you let a friend hammer a 4-inch nail into a block of pine placed on the books! Because of their inertia, the heavy books move sluggishly when the nail is struck; therefore they cushion the blows.

In the second, inertia helps you drive a similar nail through a 1-inch pine board by means of arm power alone. To do this, first cushion the head of the nail with a thick pad made of a folded handkerchief. Hold the cushioned nailhead firmly against the joint between the first and second fingers of one hand. Then grasp the wrist of that hand with the other hand, raise both hands above your head, and bring the nail down rapidly with a full arm swing. The inertia of your swift-moving hands and arms should force the nail right through the board!

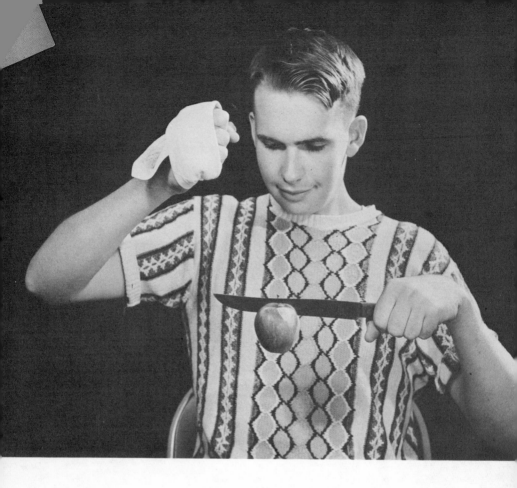

Inertia Helps Halve an Apple

Swordsmen of bygone days sometimes tested their skill by trying to cleave small objects tossed into the air. With a good eye, a swift blow, and the help of inertia, they often succeeded.

Although swords are no longer common at the dinner table, you can easily perform a modified version of this ancient sport with an apple and a carving knife. You can cut the apple in two without resting it on anything!

Here's how: Wrap one hand with a napkin and hold the knife and the apple with the other, pressing the knife just far enough into the apple to support it. Then bring down the free hand sharply on the end of the blade. Inertia keeps the apple from moving as fast as the knife—therefore the knife goes right through it!

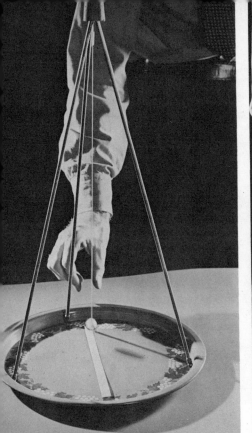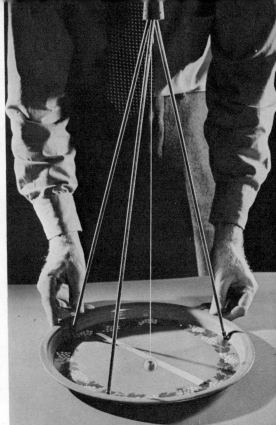

Foucault's Pendulum

Because a pendulum—due to inertia—tends to keep swinging in the same plane, we can prove that the earth revolves. The French physicist Foucault demonstrated this in 1851. He suspended a heavy ball from the dome of the Pantheon in Paris and set it swinging. The oscillations of this giant pendulum seemed to rotate in relation to the floor. By mathematics, however, Foucault showed that it was really the earth that turned.

With a marble suspended from a tripod by a thread—and the whole mounted on a tray—you can demonstrate this principle. Start the marble swinging over a marked path on the tray. Then, to represent the rotation of the earth, turn the tray slowly. You will observe that the plane of swing remains constant while the marked path changes.

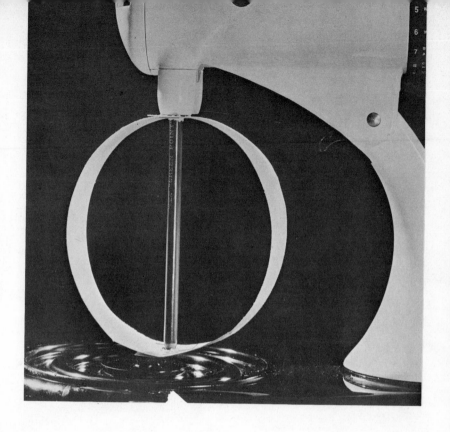

How the Earth Got Its Bulge

Why does the earth bulge through its middle? How does a cowboy spin his lariat? How can milk be separated from cream by whirling? How does your washer spin-dry clothes?

With the help of your electric mixer—plus a few gadgets you can make in minutes from tin cans, string, cardboard, and other materials found around the house—you can find out for yourself. When you are through experimenting, you can instantly reconvert the mixer to beat up a batch of waffles! (Stunts for another session of fun with your mixer begin on page 134.)

According to schoolbooks, the earth's diameter is about 26 miles greater through the equator than it is along its axis from pole to pole. Maybe your mixer can show you why.

Make a loop by gluing together the ends of a strip of stiff paper about 16 inches long and 1 inch wide. Mount this loop on a pencil that fits snugly into one of the mixer chucks, as shown above. The

hole at the top of the loop should grip the pencil tightly; the one at the bottom should fit it loosely.

When at rest, the loop forms a circle. If you start it spinning, however, it begins to bulge. Spin it faster, and it bulges still more (photo above).

The reason? Again inertia. Inertia tends not only to keep a moving body moving at a constant rate, but to keep it moving in a *straight line*. The *centrifugal*, or "center-fleeing," *force* that pulls out the loop when it spins is really the pull exerted by inertia in its effort to make the sides of the loop move straight ahead. The faster the spin, the greater the pull.

Centrifugal force pulls similarly on the earth as it spins on its axis. Although the earth is made of pretty rigid stuff, the force is enormous enough to pull it measurably out of shape.

Centrifuges and Cream Separators

If two bodies of different weight are whirled in a circle at the same speed, the heavier one will push outward with greater force than the lighter. This principle is used in centrifuges to separate solids from liquids or a liquid of one density from that of another. A cream separator is a type of centrifuge which separates heavy milk from lighter cream by whirling whole milk at high speed.

How a centrifuge works can be shown by spinning a small round-bottomed flask containing a little water and a small quantity of fine lead shot. Couple the flask to the mixer by means of a short pencil passed through a hole in the stopper. Center the flask exactly and make all fittings tight. Then start the mixer and speed it up gradually. When the speed is high enough, the heavy shot will form a ring around the widest part of the flask, while the water will form a band inside this ring, nearer the center!

Centrifugal Force Dries Your Clothes

Centrifugal force is used to dry clothes in many home washing machines. It is also used to dry sugar, salt, and other crystalline substances in the preparation of foods and chemicals.

With the help of your mixer and a squat coffee can, you can show how centrifugal drying works. With a nail, punch the sides of the can full of holes; then suspend the can by three cords from a spindle (described on the next page) attached to the mixer.

To work your drier, place a piece of wet cloth in the can, lower the can into the center of a circular enclosure made of cardboard, and run the mixer at high speed. Water from the cloth is flung out through the holes in the can and forms a ring around the inside of the enclosure, as shown in the photograph above.

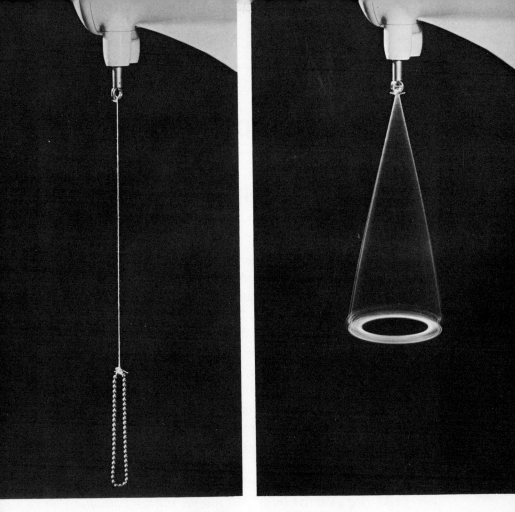

U. S. 1304153

How a Cowboy Spins His Lariat

Spinning a lariat is another extraordinary feat made possible by centrifugal force. Your mixer may help show you how.

A 2-inch length of round pencil which fits the mixer chuck snugly and is provided at one end with a screw eye makes a spindle to which you can attach a miniature "lariat." The latter consists of a 3-inch loop of beaded chain tied to a 6-inch string.

As you speed up the mixer, centrifugal force raises the bottom of the loop higher and higher. Finally it causes the loop to spin horizontally in a perfect circle. In this position, the weight of the loop is as far as possible from its axis of rotation.

LAMPWICKS AND LIQUID SPHERES

Why Drops Are Spherical

Tiny raindrops falling freely through the air take the form of spheres. If somehow we could relieve them from the distorting effects of gravity and other external forces, *all* isolated bodies of liquid—big or little—would become spherical!

You can demonstrate this beautifully by floating drops of oil in a mixture of alcohol and water. Use a flat-sided bottle so that the drops won't appear distorted. Fill it about two-thirds full of rubbing alcohol (either ethyl or isopropyl alcohol will do), and into this put a few drops of cooking oil. Then slowly add water until the drops float midway in the bottle.

To prove that the drops will remain spherical, regardless of size, enlarge some by injecting more oil into them with a medicine dropper. You should end up with a miniature planetary system of liquid spheres, like that shown on the opposite page.

Why do liquids—unless pulled out of shape by outside forces— always take this globular form? Because of *surface tension.*

To understand how surface tension works, imagine a molecule of liquid that has wandered to the surface. There the molecule is tugged at by similar molecules inside the liquid and on each side of it, but by almost none outside the liquid. As a result of this inward and sideways pull, the liquid surface tends to contract, as if it were the stretched rubber of a toy balloon. Because a sphere has the smallest surface for a given volume, the surface tension on a body of free liquid always tries to form a sphere.

In the case of a small droplet floating in the air or resting on a surface it doesn't wet, surface tension is stronger than outside forces and so succeeds in its aim. If a droplet *wets* a surface, however, adhesion to the surface flattens it out. Larger bodies of liquids are flattened by gravity, and also by adhesion if the liquid wets the surface on which it rests.

36

Surface Tension Tames a Cork

Fill a small glass nearly full of water and float a cork on the water. Then challenge a party guest to make the cork stay at the middle of the surface. No matter how carefully he places it, the cork will always dart quickly to one side of the glass!

How can it be tamed? By adding more water until the surface is slightly heaped up. The cork will then dash to the center!

Why? In the first case, water climbs up around the cork and at the edge of the glass, producing a concave surface between them. In trying to shorten this surface, surface tension lifts it. As the water in the raised portion is at less pressure than that of the air (and as the water can never be raised to exactly the same level on all sides of the cork), air pressure pushes the cork toward the side where the surface is highest. When the water edge curves down-ward, pressures are balanced with the cork in the middle.

Hot Water Leaks Faster Than Cold

The mystery of the car radiator that leaks when the water it contains is hot and seems intact when the water is cold can be explained by the laws of molecular motion. When water is cold, its molecules hug each other closely and move about slowly. Heating the water speeds up their motion and permits them to slide over each other freely. In viscous liquids, such as heavy oil or molasses, the effect of temperature is obvious. But even in liquids as thin as water, heat has the same effect.

As a demonstration, make a hole with a very fine needle in the bottom of each of two identical cans. In one place ice water and in the other the same amount of hot water. Set each over a glass and watch the race. The hot water flows much faster. In fact, if the hole is small enough and the water not too high, the cold water may not flow at all.

A Camphor-chip Ballet

Chips scraped from a block of gum camphor will dart about crazily if allowed to fall on the surface of clean water in a bowl. Their motive power is derived from differences in surface tension produced as the rough edges of the camphor dissolve at an uneven rate.

To stop this camphor ballet instantly, all you need do is touch the tip of one finger to the surface of the water. Unless you have washed your hands quite recently or have an unusually dry skin, enough oil will flow from that single touch to cover the water and send the camphor scurrying to one side of the bowl.

The Unwettable Hand

Here's a bit of science magic for little boys who hate to wash their hands and grownups who would like to amaze their friends. By means of it you can dip your hand into a bowl of ordinary water and bring it out perfectly dry!

The secret? First rub thoroughly into your hand a little zinc stearate bath powder. If you do this carefully, the powder will not be seen. Then dip your hand into the water and withdraw it quickly. The water will roll off your hand as off a duck's back.

Water ordinarily wets your hand because water molecules are attracted more strongly to your hand than to each other. It rolls off when you apply zinc stearate because water molecules are attracted more to each other than they are to this greasy powder.

41

A Sieve Holds Water

Your friends won't believe you when you tell them that you can hold a glass of water upside down, with nothing but a piece of handkerchief, laid over the top, to keep the water from tumbling out. Yet—with the aid of surface tension and atmospheric pressure —this feat is not difficult to perform.

After partly or wholly filling the glass, lay a piece of wet hand-kerchief over the mouth, smoothing it down over the sides of the glass and making sure that it touches the edge at all points. Then, with your hand over the cloth, invert the glass and carefully remove your hand. Does the water fall out? No! Air pressure holds the cloth to the glass, while surface tension keeps the water from seeping through.

Why Liquids Rise in Plants and Wicks

Wipe your hands on a towel, and the towel dries them; put the stems of flowers in water, and the blossoms revive; immerse the lower end of a lampwick in oil, and the oil climbs to the top.

A simple stunt may help show you why. Fasten together two sheets of clean glass with cellulose tape, first separating them slightly at one edge with a strip of thin cardboard. Then stand the sheets of glass, as shown above, in a dish of water.

Immediately, because of the combined forces of adhesion and surface tension, the water climbs between the glass sheets—rising highest where the surfaces are closest together.

Water climbs thus in the capillary, or "hairlike," tubes in the fibers of towels and plants, and oil in such tubes in the fibers of wicks. The finer the tubes, the higher the liquid climbs.

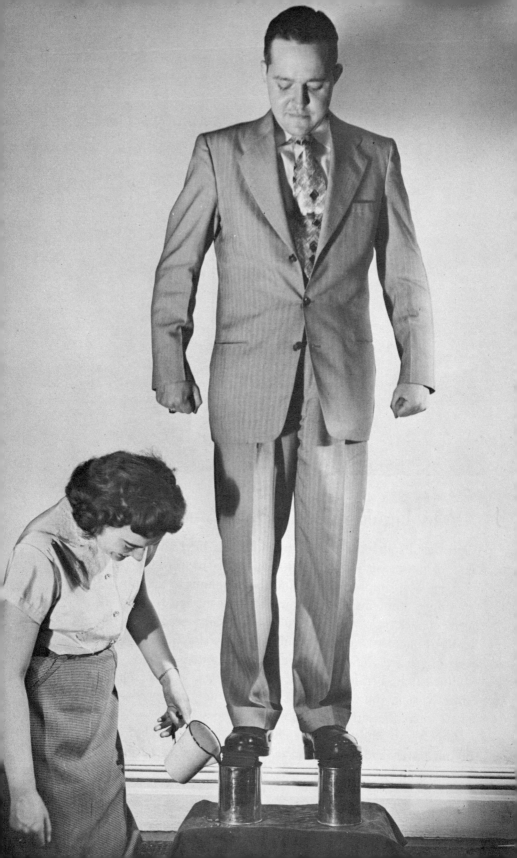

A Capillary Samson

Water not only rises in capillary tubes, but often exerts incredible force in doing so. Wedges of dry wood driven into holes in rock can drink in water so forcefully that they split the rock. Clotheslines, too taut when dry, sometimes pull out their supporting hooks when rain causes their fibers to thicken and shorten.

A story is told concerning the erection, in 1586, of the obelisk which still stands in front of St. Peter's in Rome. In hoisting the heavy stone to mount it, the ropes had stretched so much that the base of the column could not quite reach the top of the pedestal. Just as the architect Fontana was about to give up, someone among the spectators shouted: "Wet the ropes!" When this advice had been carried out, the obelisk rose slowly to the required height.

You can demonstrate the might with which water can force its way into the minute tubes in porous materials by the stunt shown on the facing page.

Cut enough squares of porous cardboard to fill two similar tin cans to the brim. After stacking the squares in the cans, stand on the cans and have a friend fill the space remaining in them with water. (A little soapless detergent stirred in the water will speed its penetration.)

As the water forces its way into the pores of the cardboard by capillary attraction, it causes the cardboard to swell. Soon you will find yourself lifted bodily several inches above the tops of the cans, as shown below.

Jonah Swallows a Whale

Would you believe you could cram the great wad of cotton in the left hand of our friend above into the tiny glass of water in his right—and do so without losing a drop of water? It sounds incredible, but it can be done.

Fill the glass with water to within ⅛ inch of the top. Put the fluffed-out cotton, bit by bit, into the glass, pressing it down with a toothpick or stirring rod. With care, you can squeeze it all into the glass without causing the water to overflow.

How is this possible? Absorbent materials, such as cotton, consist chiefly of air cells surrounded by an exceedingly small amount of solid substance. When such materials are immersed, water fills the cells, and only their solid substance takes up space.

46

Geber's Capillary Filter

Salt dissolved in water will climb in wicks and capillary tubes along with the water; insoluble substances, mixed in water, will be left behind. Back in the eighth century, the Arabian alchemist Geber used this fact as the basis of an ingenious filter for separating undissolved substances from solutions.

You can demonstrate Geber's device with the setup shown above. Half fill the top glass with a solution of calcium chloride and the middle one with a solution of sodium carbonate. Then connect the glasses with pieces of twisted cloth, thoroughly wet.

The first cloth siphons calcium chloride solution from the top glass into the middle glass. There the calcium chloride combines with the sodium carbonate to form chalk. As chalk is insoluble, the second cloth siphons a clear solution into the final glass.

FLUID MECHANICS

Perpetual Motion?

Can water keep going round and round through a system of containers and tubes, without the application of external power? In a paradoxical device invented some twenty centuries ago by Heron of Alexandria, it seems to do just that!

On the opposite page is shown a homemade version of *Heron's fountain*. To start it, you merely pour half a glass of water into the funnel. Water rises in the outlet tube from the upper can and squirts from the tip. By aiming the tip so the water falls into the funnel, the flow will go on and on.

What keeps the gadget going? Your most intelligent friends will probably give you the wildest answers!

Most observers who guess wrong assume that the water makes a complete circuit. It doesn't—as you can see from the diagram below. At the start, the upper can is filled with water; the lower can is left empty. The water poured through the funnel into the lower can displaces some of the air in the can. This air goes up the connecting tube and forces water out of the upper can. Thus, instead of lifting water from the table level, the apparatus merely lifts it from the height of the upper can!

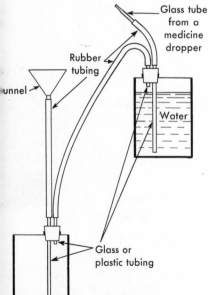

Glass tube from a medicine dropper

Rubber tubing

unnel

Water

Glass or plastic tubing

The flow will of course stop when the top can is empty; to start again switch cans.

You can easily make this device by following the diagram and the photograph. Any two similar cans which can be closed with stoppers will do. Fit each stopper with a long and a short glass or plastic tube, as shown in the diagram. Connections—which must be airtight—may be made with rubber bath-spray hose. The glass tube from a medicine dropper makes an excellent outlet jet.

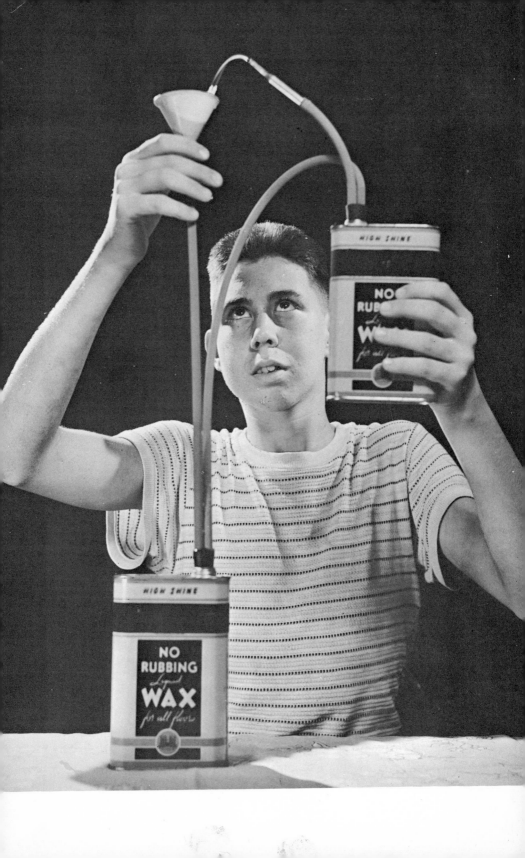

Aerosol Bombs Work by Gas Pressure

Just press a button on the can-type dispensing devices, and out squirts insecticide, fire-extinguishing fluid, whipped cream, or what have you. The push behind the squirt is compressed gas.

How compressed gas can propel a liquid may be shown by a trick with a surprise ending. Attach a rubber tube about 8 inches long to the large end of the glass tube from a medicine dropper. Pass the tip of the glass tube through a hole in a cork, and insert the cork tightly in a soda bottle about two-thirds full of water.

Now ask a friend to test his lungs by blowing as many bubbles as he can through the water. The more air he forces into the bottle, the higher the water will squirt when he removes his mouth!

Air Pressure Works This Elevator

Cork one end of a long glass tube ¾ inch in diameter, fill it with water, and insert a small stoppered vial until its top is depressed even with the top of the tube. Now place your hand over the top of the tube, invert it over a dish to catch the water, and remove your hand.

Does the vial fall out? Not at all. It rises!

Why? Because water running out around the vial prevents air from getting into the upper part of the tube. As a result, the pressure below the vial (atmospheric pressure) is always greater than the pressure above it (produced by the weight of the water). Air pressure, therefore, pushes the vial up the tube.

A Cup for Tantalus

Tantalus, so the legend goes, was a Lydian king who displeased the gods. As punishment, the gods plunged him up to his chin in a river in Hades; then, as an added torment, they rigged this river so that every time Tantalus bent over to drink, its waters receded!

With a funnel, a bit of rubber tubing, and a plastic straw, you can make a mystifying device which will duplicate, in a fashion, the tantalizing behavior of that mythical river.

Soften the straw in hot water; then bend one end of it as shown above. Slip the short rubber tube over the straight portion (to seal the connection) and fit the combination into the funnel.

If you now pour water into the funnel slowly enough, the funnel will never fill! Every time the water reaches the top of the bend, it starts to siphon off; and it doesn't stop siphoning until it reaches the bottom. The cycle then repeats itself.

Intermittent springs often work on the same principle.

A Milk-bottle Barometer

Do you know how a barometer measures the changing pressure of the atmosphere? Maybe you can get a better idea by making the simple milk-bottle version shown above.

Cut the end from a round toy balloon. Then stretch this end smoothly over the mouth of a milk bottle and tie it in place. Next fasten one end of a drinking straw to the center of the rubber cap with a drop of sealing wax. For a scale, mark a strip of cardboard with graduations and prop it up beside the straw.

Compare the position of the straw pointer from day to day. When the atmospheric pressure rises, it pushes the rubber cap *in*; when it falls, the greater pressure inside the bottle pushes the cap *out*. Always take your readings when the air is at the same temperature; otherwise they will be unreliable.

Ammonia Makes a Fountain

Compared with the ability of ammonia gas to squeeze its way into water, the feat of the twenty-odd circus cops who crowd blithely into a taxi hardly big enough for one is nothing at all. At room temperature, about 700 volumes of ammonia can fit comfortably in 1 volume of H_2O!

This amazing affinity of water for gas is used to help condense ammonia in the gas refrigerator. At the dinner table or the chemistry club you can use it to produce the spectacular fountain-in-a-bottle shown on the opposite page.

All the equipment you need—besides a glass of water and a small wad of wet cotton—is shown below. Push a thin glass or plastic tube, about 9 inches long, through a tight-fitting hole in a cork until half of the tube projects on each side. Then put 2 ounces of household ammonia into an 8-ounce soda bottle, stopper the bottle with the cork (the tube should not dip into the ammonia), and stand the bottle aslant in a pot of water over a heater.

When bubbles appear in the ammonia, hold a large soda bottle (use a soda bottle, as other bottles may prove too weak) over the outer end of the tube to catch the gas. When a strong whiff of ammonia tells you the bottle is full, remove the bottle carefully—

keeping it inverted. Then remove the cork from the small bottle, wrap the wet cotton around the tube next to the small end of the cork, and insert the cork tightly in the large bottle.

Now quickly place the lower end of the tube into the glass of water. As ammonia dissolves in the wet cotton, a partial vacuum is produced and water climbs up the tube. As soon as a few drops emerge from the top, more ammonia dissolves. Soon the vacuum becomes so great that water squirts up in a powerful gusher.

54

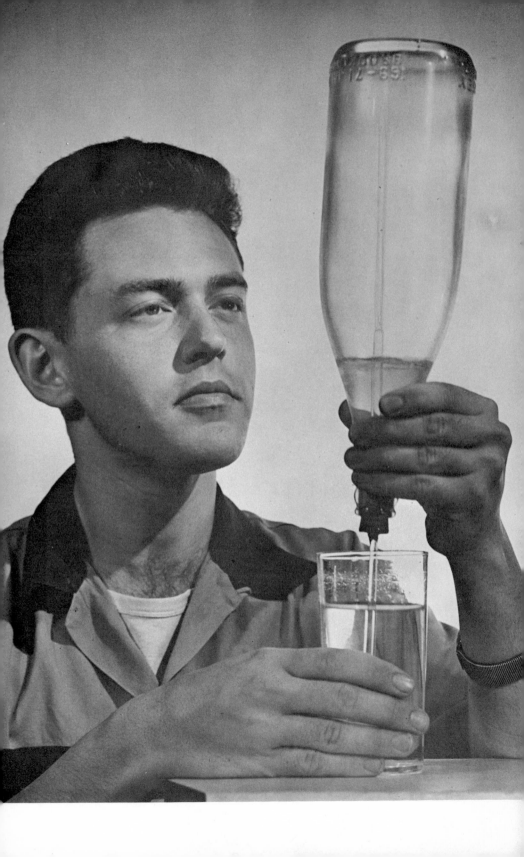

You Can't Compress Water

Glass bottles are made of quite rigid stuff, but nevertheless you can squeeze one with your hands far more successfully than you can the water in it. As this stunt takes a little muscular prowess, it can also be used to determine the Samson of the group.

Completely fill a quart bottle with water and close it with a stopper through which has been passed, tip upward, the glass tube from a medicine dropper. Press down the stopper until the water rises nearly to the top of the tube. Then squeeze with all your might. If you apply enough force, the water rises in the tube and may even overflow. This incompressibility of water makes it useful for transmitting force undiminished in hydraulic systems.

The Obedient Diver

A medicine dropper, a bottle of water, and a cork are all you need to make a mystifying diver that will sink or rise at your command. Descartes invented its ancestor more than 300 years ago.

Fill the bottle to the brim. Fill the dropper so that it just barely floats, bulb end up. Then put the dropper into the bottle and insert the cork.

To make your diver sink, press on the cork; to make it float, loosen the cork. As water can't be compressed, it rises in the dropper and squeezes the air at the top, making the dropper less buoyant. The air expands again when you release the pressure.

Lift Books with Your Breath

Next time someone remarks that so-and-so's breath "could knock you over," don't jump to conclusions; if the speaker is a scientist, he may be stating a simple fact!

The present stunt may convince you. Pile heavy books on an empty syringe-type hot-water bottle. Fit a short glass tube, for a mouthpiece, to a rubber tube, and attach the other end of the rubber tube to the bottle. Then, while a friend steadies the books, start blowing. With little effort, you can lift them all!

The reason? Although your breath exerts only a few ounces of pressure at the end of the tube, this pressure is transmitted equally to equal areas all over the inside of the bottle. Thus the lifting force of your breath is greatly magnified. If the bottle were large enough, your breath could topple the heaviest man.

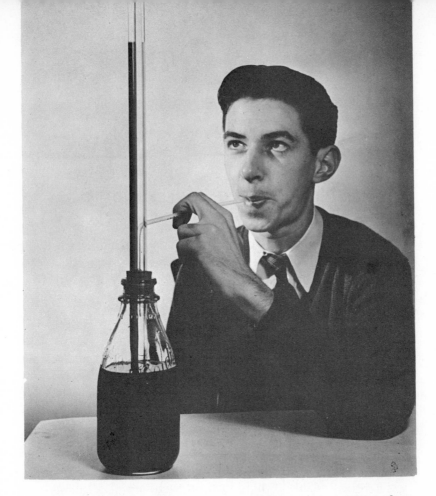

Breath Can Support Different Weights

You can lift 1 pound or 10 pounds with the same breath pressure (or with the same pressure of any confined gas or liquid), provided the area on which it pushes is ten times as great in the second case as in the first. This fact can be shown visually.

Push two long glass or plastic tubes of different diameters through holes in a cork, so that they extend about 6 inches beyond the small end. Push a shorter tube, bent at right angles, through a third hole, just far enough to reach the other side. Then insert the stopper in a milk bottle two-thirds full of water colored with ink.

If you now blow into the bent tube, air pressure at the top of the bottle will force the inky water up the straight tubes. Odd as it may seem, the water will rise as high in the large tube as it does in the small one!

FLUIDS IN MOTION

Low Fluid Pressure Works Magic

Strange as it may seem, the pressure inside a tornado is less than the pressure of calm air; the pressure inside a raging stream is less than that in a still pond!

You can demonstrate this paradox, and have fun at the same time, by performing the stunts shown on the facing page.

The first can be made into an amusing party game. Provide each contestant with a Ping-pong ball and a glass or plastic tube bent into the form of an "L." By blowing strongly enough and steadily enough into the long end of the tube, he can keep the ball supported in the air stream above the short end. The windiest and most self-controlled contestant will, of course, be the winner.

Why does the ball stay in the stream? Because the air in the stream is at lower pressure than the still air beside it; when the ball tries to escape, the outside air pushes it back.

As a sequel, bend down ½ inch on each end of a calling card, place the card on a table, and challenge a guest to blow it over. If he blows under it, the card will cling to the table as if glued—the still air above the card being at greater pressure than the moving air beneath it. To overturn it, the guest must blow just above and parallel with the top of the card.

That the pressure inside a stream of water is also lower than that of still air can be proved by two stunts you can perform at the kitchen sink. In the first, hold a marble inside an inverted funnel connected by a rubber tube to the faucet. Then turn on the water and remove your hand. Instead of falling out, the marble clings close to the neck—air pressure below it being greater than the water pressure between the marble and the sides of the funnel!

As a finale, attach a string to a Ping-pong ball and place the ball under a stream of water. Even if you hold the string at a considerable angle, the ball will cling to the stream!

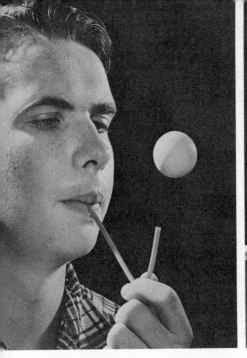

If you blow hard enough, the ball will stay in the stream.

To overturn this card, you must know a trick of science.

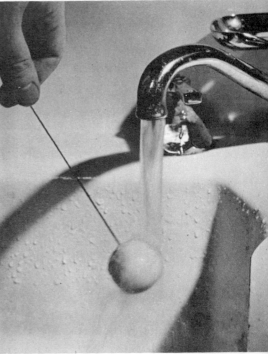

Air pressure supports a marble against the pull of gravity.

Air pressure holds a ball against a stream of water.

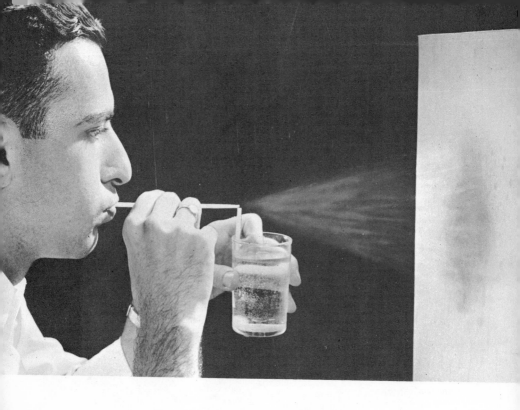

Spray Guns and Carburetors

The principle that the faster a fluid moves, the less the pressure is inside the fluid—first noted by Daniel Bernoulli in 1738—is today used in designing paint and insecticide sprays, atomizers, and carburetors for cars.

You can show how these devices work with the help of two halves of a soda straw and a glass of water.

After flattening one end of each straw, stand one straw in the water and hold the other horizontally, flattened ends together. Then blow hard through the horizontal straw, aiming the air from it directly across the tip of the other. Water will climb up in the vertical straw, emerge at the top, and spray out.

The secret? Air speeding over the tip of the vertical straw is at a lower pressure than that of the atmosphere. Atmospheric pressure therefore pushes water from the glass up into the air stream.

Atomizers, spray guns, and carburetors work similarly when a stream of air is forced across the upper end of a tube whose lower end dips in perfume, paint, insecticide, or gasoline.

A Tube Loops the Loop

The curved path of spinning baseballs, tennis balls, and golf balls is explained by unbalanced air pressure, due to the difference in speed of the air around their two sides. Rotation causes air to pass more swiftly around one side than the other. The balls naturally curve toward the side where the air speed is higher and, hence, the pressure is lower.

A hint of the spectacular curves these balls might make if they were lighter or could be spun faster can be shown with the help of a ribbon and a light cardboard tube.

If it is thin enough, the core of a roll of paper toweling should serve nicely for the tube. After making a small loop in a yard length of ½-inch ribbon, wind the rest of it around the middle of the tube. Then lay the tube on a table and pass the end of a stick through the loop, as shown above.

Now give the stick a quick jerk forward. If the tube is light enough and the jerk is fast enough, the tube will rise gracefully in the air and perform several complete loops before it falls!

A Turbine Top

Your grandfather performed a feat of science magic that is as amazing today as it was seventy-five years ago. He placed a calling card (with a pin through its center to keep it from sideslipping) against one end of a spool and blew hard through the other end.

Could he blow the card off? Never! The harder he blew, the tighter the card hugged the spool. When he aimed the spool downward, the card defied gravity as well as the impact of his breath!

This stunt also depends upon unbalanced pressure. Air speeding between the card and the end of the spool is at lower pressure than the still air beneath the card; the still air therefore holds the card against the spool.

A toy top which adds the principle of the turbine to the effect of Bernoulli is perhaps even more astonishing.

The rotor of this device is a 3½-inch disk cut from a filing card. Six diagonal flaps are laid out on the disk, cut on three sides with a sharp knife, and bent up, as shown in the left-hand photograph below. A straight pin is pushed through the center of the disk, leaving ¼ inch projecting below to serve as a pivot. A little sealing wax is applied around the pivot to hold the pin in place.

To work your turbine, hold the disk lightly against one end of a spool, letting the pin enter the hole. Then blow through the other end. The disk will spin rapidly—the stream of air that spins it also holding it against the spool—as shown on page 65. If you then hold the whirling disk near a table and stop blowing, the disk will fall from the spool, but will continue to spin like a top, as shown below, right.

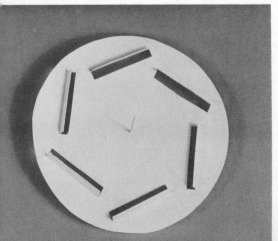

SOUND AND VIBRATION

A Soda-straw Orchestra

Your friends will laugh when you tell them you can make a musical instrument from a straw; they will laugh harder when you play it!

To make this rudimentary reed pipe, just flatten ½ inch of one end of the straw and cut off about ¼ inch from each corner (as shown below). To play it, insert 1½ inches into your mouth; then close your lips and blow hard. You should get a strong musical note —about as pleasant and as penetrating as a New Year's horn!

You can raise the straw's pitch (on up to that of a peanut whistle) merely by cutting off pieces from its outer end. By thus tuning straws to different musical tones, you can produce an impromptu "orchestra" to entertain at the dinner table, party, or club—each man playing his own note when it comes due!

Your musical straw is a simplified version of the clarinet, the saxophone, and of certain musical automobile horns. Air from your breath causes the flaps on the straw to flutter (just as it flutters the reed in a real musical instrument). This fluttering, in turn, causes the air column in the straw to vibrate at a frequency determined by the length of the straw (or the instrument). The shorter the air column, the higher is this frequency.

To find out what the flare on the end adds to a wind instrument, place funnels of different sizes over the end of your straw. By directing the sound waves and providing more air for them to push against, the funnels amplify the sound.

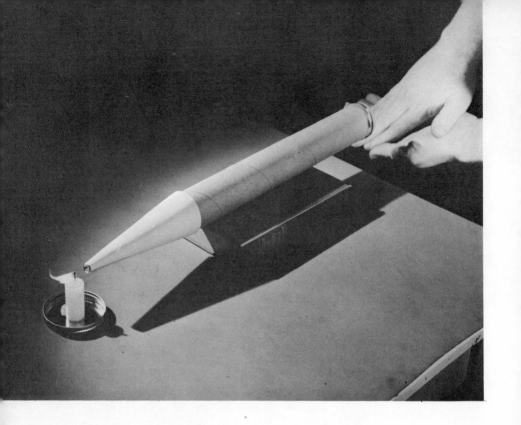

Sound Waves Are Physical Impulses

You can prove that sound is transmitted by physical vibrations by actually causing sound waves to blow a candle flame—after they have passed through a solid partition!

Make a cone of paper with an opening about ¼ inch across at the small end and fasten it to one end of a mailing tube about 2 feet long. Over the other end of the tube stretch tightly a piece of rubber cut from a toy balloon. Then support the tube so that the opening of the cone comes as near as possible (without catching fire) to the flame of a candle.

Now clap your hands smartly together close to the balloon end of the tube. Although no air from your hands can enter the tube, the candle flame nevertheless flutters wildly. Sound waves from the clap cause the diaphragm to vibrate. This, in turn, passes on the vibrations to the air particles in the tube.

68

A Church Bell from a Spoon

Would you believe you could get a loud, clear, bell-like sound from a spoon? If not, here is a stunt that should change your mind.

Tie a dessertspoon, so that it just balances, to the middle of a 4-foot length of thin wire (thin string will do, but the effect will be weaker). Then—holding the ends of the wire in your ears—let the spoon strike the edge of a table. You will hear the deep, sonorous tone of a church bell!

To hear a higher note, substitute a teaspoon; to hear a lower one, a tablespoon. All the tones will be loud and pleasing.

Because they are curved and vary in thickness, spoons, like bells, produce complex sounds which are rich in overtones. The wires make these sounds louder by conducting them directly to your ears.

Dry Ice Makes a Fork Sing

Strike a fork on the edge of a table and it will sing forth a musical note. The pitch of this note is determined by the natural frequency of vibration of the fork.

If you want the fork to sing louder and longer, however, just rub its edge lightly along a bit of dry ice (held with a cloth or tongs). Imperfect contact with the intense cold (about 110 degrees below zero, Fahrenheit) of the solid carbon dioxide causes the metal to contract and expand rapidly. This sets the fork vibrating at its natural frequency. As long as you hold it against the cold substance it keeps up its piercing cry.

A Reflector Focuses Sound

Sound waves—especially those of high pitch—can be reflected and focused like waves of light and heat. Dome-shaped reflectors over outdoor concert platforms thus help direct music toward the audience. Sounding boards above pulpits similarly amplify a speaker's voice by concentrating it in a single direction.

With the help of a watch, a bowl-type electric heater, and a large cone (with its tip cut off) made of cardboard, you can demonstrate how the reflection and focusing of sound works.

Suspend the watch so that it hangs close to the center of the reflector. Then put the small end of the cone to your ear and aim the wide end toward the reflector. If the position of the watch is correct, you will hear its ticks many feet away. This is because the reflector concentrates the sound into a parallel beam.

Famous Curves Analyze Vibrations

Nearly a hundred years ago, the French scientist Lissajous attached tiny mirrors to tuning forks arranged at right angles to each other. Then he shot a ray of light onto one mirror so that it was reflected to the other and from there onto a screen. When the forks were set vibrating, their combined motion caused the ray of light to trace out a simple or intricate pattern on the screen.

These *Lissajous curves* were not only beautiful and fascinating, but their patterns were clues to the exact relationship between the pitch and other qualities of the waves from the two forks. Lissajous' method for comparing sound waves still ranks among the best.

By substituting a simple two-way pendulum for the tuning forks, and a trail of salt for the path of the ray of light, you can see for yourself how these amazing patterns are made.

Construction of the pendulum is shown on the opposite page. It consists of two 3-foot lengths of string, attached about a foot apart to an overhead support, and formed into a "Y" by means of a loop of string tied around them part way down. The weight is a paper drinking cup (or other paper cone) with a ¼-inch hole cut in its tip. A square of cardboard catches the pattern of salt.

To make your curves, partly fill the cup with salt, draw it to one corner of the cardboard, and let it go. The curve produced depends upon the relative length of the two parts of the "Y." By sliding the binding loop up or down, you can change the design.

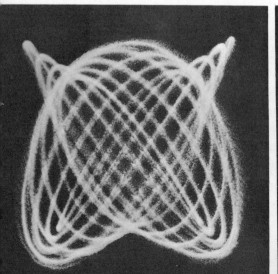

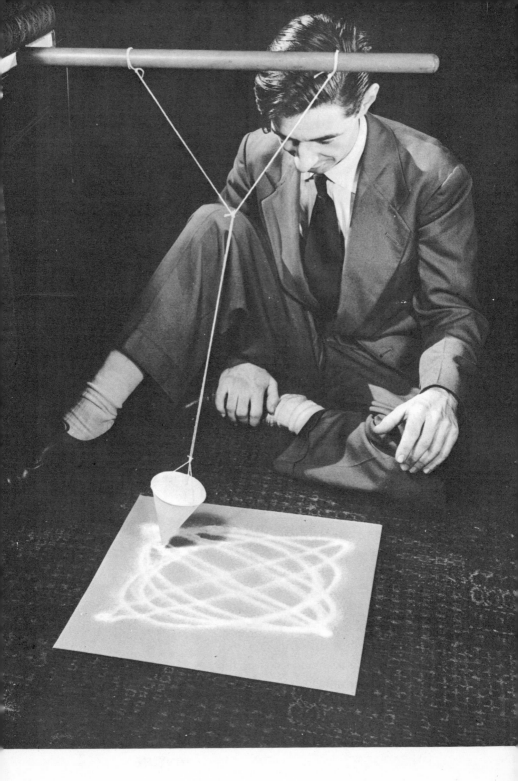

You can make dozens of intricate salt patterns with this compound pendulum. To change the design, shift the juncture of the "Y."

LITTLE BROTHER OF LIGHTNING

Static Is Everywhere

Maybe you have never thought of yourself as an electric generator. Yet, every time you walk across a rug, comb your hair, lift a paper from your desk, or run your car over a road—in fact, every time you lift anything from anything, or rub something against something else—you conjure up a charge of static electricity!

In summer, when most surfaces are moist, this static leaks off so fast it isn't noticed. On a dry winter day, however, you meet its snaps, cracks, sparks, and jolts at every turn.

To show how electricity can be produced from almost nowhere, hold two long strips of newspaper together by one end and give them several light downward strokes between the thumb and forefinger of your free hand. The strips fly apart! Charged similarly by contact with your fingers, they repel each other.

Where does the charge come from? When two different substances are pressed together, free electrons are pulled over from the substance which has the weaker attraction for them to the one which has the stronger. When the substances are then separated, the one which has lost electrons carries a positive charge, while the other carries a negative charge.

You can produce positive and negative charges to order by rubbing together and then separating any two of the substances mentioned at the right. The substance higher in the list will become positive and the lower one negative. The farther apart the substances are on the list, the greater will be the charge.

PHOTO FILM

POLISHED GLASS

WOOL

NYLON

COTTON

SILK

LUCITE

SEALING WAX

POLYSTYRENE

HARD RUBBER

VINYLITE

74

A Chewing-gum-wrapper Electroscope

Are your phonograph records, combs, draperies—or perhaps even your party guests!—charged with static electricity? If they are, what is their charge—positive or negative?

With the help of a simple electroscope, or "charge detector," which you can make from the everyday materials shown above, you can quickly find out!

The telltale indicator of this sensitive device consists of two strips of aluminum foil hung face to face at the end of a nail which is insulated from the ground. A charged object brought near the head of the nail will induce a charge on the nail and the foil. As both leaves will be charged with electricity of the same sign, they will repel each other; the greater the charge, the farther the leaves will fly apart.

The completed electroscope is shown in the photograph at the top of the next page. To assemble it, first make a ½-inch hole in the top of the mayonnaise jar. Then melt the end of a stick of sealing wax and apply a blob of it around the nail, about 1 inch from the head. While the wax is still soft, insert the nail through the hole in the jar top and press the wax against both sides of the hole. Keep the nail centered until the wax hardens.

You can get thin aluminum foil for the leaves from a chewing-gum wrapper. Remove the paper attached to this foil by first soaking the wrapper in rubbing alcohol and then rubbing the paper off with your fingers.

From the bare foil, cut two strips ½ inch wide and 3 inches long. Place these together and tie their upper ends against the lower end of the nail with a piece of thread.

To use your electroscope to tell whether the charge on an object is positive or negative, first give the electroscope a negative charge by touching its knob (the nailhead) with a hard rubber comb or a vinylite record that has been rubbed with wool. This will cause the leaves to separate.

If you now bring a negatively charged body near the knob, the leaves will separate still farther, while a positively charged body will cause them to come together.

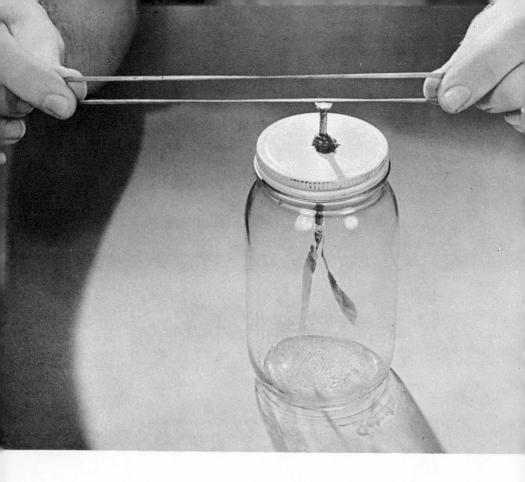

Stretching Rubber Produces Static

Static electricity may be generated in more ways than by separating two substances or by rubbing them together. You can electrify rubber, for example, *merely by stretching it!*

If you doubt this, stretch a dry rubber band and touch it to the knob of your electroscope. The leaves will separate! Pull the band along the knob, and the leaves will diverge more and more.

Now discharge the stretched band by drawing it across a grounded pipe, and then let it contract. If you touch it again to the electroscope knob, the separated leaves will come together: contraction has charged the band with static of the opposite sign!

Static similarly produced by the constant flexing of inner tubes is a cause of crackles in car radios. Antistatic powder, made of a conductive material such as carbon black, helps drain it off.

Where Shall You Hide?

Where is the best place to hide from static? Inside a thick rubber ball? Never! The best place to be secure against any form of static manifestation—including lightning—is inside a completely enclosed conductor or a cage made of conducting material!

Because static charges remain entirely outside such an enclosure, metal airplanes can go right through electrified clouds—or even be hit by lightning!—without the occupants experiencing any sensation. Steel-framed skyscrapers may be struck by lightning without enough charge getting inside to affect a sensitive electroscope. On a smaller scale, radio and other electronic parts are enclosed in metal boxes to shield them from outside static.

That such shielding against static really works can be proved by placing your electroscope in a kitchen pot and covering the pot with a wire strainer. An electrified comb brought near or touched to the strainer will not affect the leaves in the least.

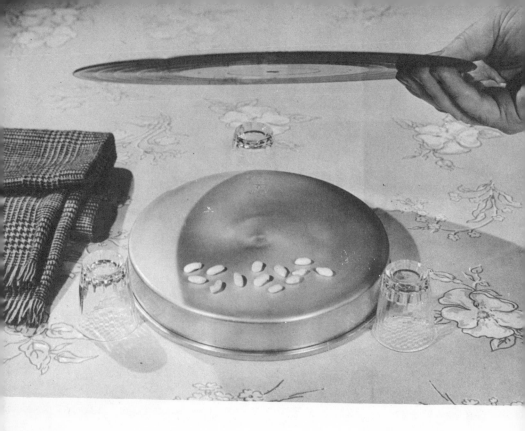

Static Makes Sandpaper and Textiles

Although static electricity is as old as creation, it has come down the centuries chiefly as a curiosity, a nuisance, and a hazard that has caused fires and taken lives.

Static electricity still cuts its freakish capers. But today, science has found means to control most of the dangerous and annoying ones. New devices now combat static with moisture, with grounding systems, by pitting static against static, and even by bombarding static fields with atomic energy. Rubber, plastics, and other materials that normally collect static charges have been made conductive to let the charges drain off.

Static has not only been tamed, but this once-useless form of electricity is now being deliberately generated to perform amazing jobs.

For example, a faster-cutting, longer-wearing sandpaper is now made by hurling grains of abrasive against adhesive-coated paper by

means of a static field. The grains all stand on end, points out, for the same reason that your hair stands on end when you comb it on a dry winter day.

Attractive imitations of embroidery are made inexpensively by similarly shooting short textile fibers at voiles and other thin materials which have been printed with an adhesive in the desired pattern. Imitation suedes and velvets, which wear longer than any comparable materials, are being turned out by the same process.

How static can make better sandpaper and textiles may be demonstrated in principle with the simple setup shown on the facing page. Puffed cereal grains are sprinkled on the bottom of an inverted cake tin. Three small glasses are arranged to support a vinylite record about ¾ inch above the tin.

If you rub the top of the record with a woolen cloth, the grains will jump to the bottom of it and hang there on end—just as the abrasive grains jump to the adhesive-coated backing in sandpaper making, and the fibers to the cloth in "electro-broidery."

The Magnetic Finger

More than 2,500 years ago, the Greek philosopher Thales discovered that amber rubbed with wool would pick up bits of thread and cloth. Ever since, the mysterious attractive force of static electricity has ranked high in the repertoire of both scientist and magician.

Here is an up-to-date party trick to carry on the tradition: Balance a pencil on an egg (or a ball, or a salt shaker). Then challenge your friends to move the pencil in a given direction without touching it, blowing on it, or jiggling the table!

When they give up, all you do is shuffle a foot on the rug (this will work only on a cold dry day) and hold a finger near the pencil. The pencil will follow your finger—attracted by the static generated by the friction between the rug and your foot.

Static Works This Pendulum

Impatient with waiting for lightning clouds to pass over his house, Franklin once rigged up a device which made them announce their presence by ringing a bell!

How this bell worked can be demonstrated by means of the lively static pendulum shown above. To make it, cover half of one side of a vinylite record with aluminum foil—securing the foil with tape. Suspend a small ball of foil by a thread.

Electrify the record by rubbing its uncoated side with wool. Then hold it as shown so that the ball is midway between the coating and the knuckles of your free hand. The ball first jumps to the coating; there it becomes charged and is repelled to your hand. Your hand discharges it, and the cycle is repeated.

In Franklin's device, an electric charge from the clouds similarly caused a small clapper to swing between two little bells.

MAGNETS AND ELECTRIC CURRENTS

A Steel Knife Short-circuits a Magnet

Strangely enough, nonmagnetic materials, such as glass, wood, and copper, permit magnetic lines of force to pass through them freely, while iron and steel often act as barriers through which the lines cannot penetrate.

You can prove this with the help of a strong horseshoe magnet, two plates of glass, and a few tacks. Separate the plates with matchsticks and place them so they form a bridge between two books, as shown below. Then stand your magnet on the upper sheet. Although separated from the magnet by a layer of air and two thicknesses of glass, tacks placed beneath and against the under sheet of glass are held to it—caught in a magnetic field that penetrates the glass-air sandwich as if it weren't there.

Now slip a steel knife blade between the sheets of glass, directly beneath the magnet, and see what happens. As the blade comes between the tacks and the magnet, the tacks drop off!

The reason? Magnetic lines travel through steel hundreds of times more readily than they do through air or glass. As a result, the knife blade short-circuits lines coming from the magnet; it carries them directly from pole to pole and allows few to escape.

By enclosing radio and other electrical coils in iron or steel casings, their external magnetism is similarly short-circuited and is thus prevented from interfering with neighboring devices.

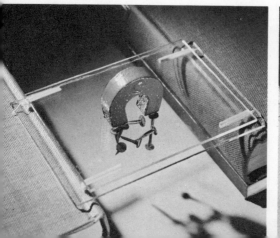
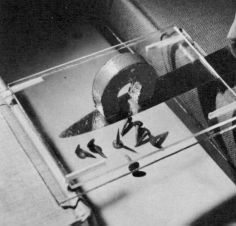

Unfriendly Nails Show a Meter Principle

Two nails and a coil of bell wire is all you need to illustrate the working mechanism of one type of a.c.-d.c. measuring instrument. Anneal the nails by heating them to redness and letting them cool slowly. Then hang them side by side on threads in the center of the coil, as shown at left above.

If you now connect the ends of the coil to three or four dry cells, the nails fly apart. Connect the ends to alternating current from a toy transformer, and again they separate. Why? Because the magnetic field set up by current passing through the coil magnetizes both nails so that each has a similar pole on the same end. Since like poles repel, the nails push each other apart. Although alternating current constantly changes its direction, the polarity of the nails changes simultaneously with it.

One form of ammeter and voltmeter depends upon this mutual repulsion between two pieces of iron within a coil of wire. One piece is fixed, while the other can rotate. The amount of its rotation is a measure of the amperage or voltage.

Which Rod Is Magnetized?

Although this puzzler involves only the simplest laws of magnetism, it has been known to stump electrical experts. Offer a friend two rods of steel (knitting needles will do) that look exactly alike. One, however, has been magnetized by rubbing it across a pole of a strong horseshoe magnet, while the other has not. Can your friend tell which is which, without using anything but the rods?

Laying the rods side by side, or touching the ends together, won't help. The attractor and the attracted have equal pull. When your friend gives up, show him how: touch the tip of one rod to the center of the other. If the tip is attracted, the rod which does the touching is the magnetized one; if it is not attracted, the touched rod is magnetized. Why? Because the pull of a magnet is concentrated near its ends; there is little or no pull at its center.

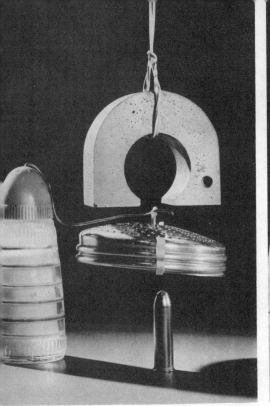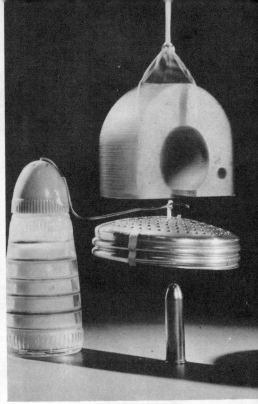

Induction Magic Works Speedometer

Ordinarily a magnet won't attract aluminum. In a common type of car speedometer, however, a magnet is caused to do just that. How this trick of magnetism works can be shown by the setup above.

Suspend the top of an aluminum flour shaker at its center from a short length of rubber band attached to a horizontal wire. Stick a bit of gummed tape on one side as a marker and stand a pencil cap beneath the marker to note its position. Directly above the shaker top hang a strong horseshoe magnet on a rubber band.

Twist the magnet a dozen times and let go. As the magnet spins, it induces electric currents in the aluminum. These currents produce a magnetic field about the top which causes it to turn in the same direction as the magnet. The faster the magnet turns, the greater is the magnetic force built up in the cap and the farther it is caused to swing.

In a speedometer a magnet connected to a flexible shaft rotates inside an aluminum cup to which the pointer is attached. A hairspring resists the turning force of the rotating magnetic field.

Six Volts Change to 120!

The ignition coil in a car takes in a 6-volt battery current at one end and sends out an 18,000-volt current (enough to produce a miniature lightning flash in the car's cylinders) at the other.

How this electrical sleight of hand works can be shown by means of an iron bolt wound with two lengths of insulated wire. Anneal the bolt by heating it red-hot and letting it cool slowly. Wind 20 turns of bell wire smoothly on the bolt as the primary. Over this wind 400 turns of finer wire as the secondary. Then connect a 115-volt neon bulb to the ends of the secondary and touch the ends of the primary momentarily to the posts of a 6-volt battery.

Each time you break the battery circuit enough voltage is induced in the secondary winding to light the neon bulb!

The boost in voltage is proportional to the ratio of the number of turns in the two windings. In your homemade coil the ratio is 1 to 20. If you put 6 volts into the primary, you should therefore get 120 volts from the secondary. To get the high voltage needed to spark your car engine, the ratio must be about 1 to 3,000.

88

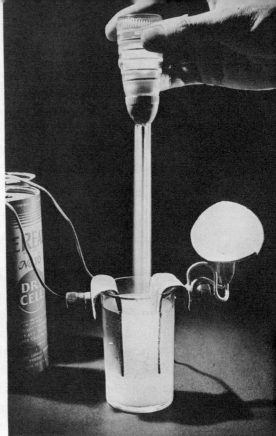

Some Solutions Conduct; Others Don't

By suspending two metal plates in a glass of water and connecting them in series with a small light bulb and several dry cells, you can divide all water-soluble substances into *electrolytes* and *nonelectrolytes*—materials that form solutions which conduct electricity and those that do not. Add sugar to the water, for instance, and the light does not glow. Add salt, and it shines brightly.

Electrolytes (salts, acids, and bases) break up into electrically charged particles, or *ions*, when dissolved. These ions carry the current. Nonelectrolytes (sugar, glycerine, alcohol) do not form ions. Besides conducting electricity, electrolytes lower the freezing point and raise the boiling point of water more than nonelectrolytes do and, in addition, are far more active chemically.

A Storage Battery in a Jiffy

Strangely enough, the storage battery in your car or your home lighting plant doesn't really "store" electricity. It merely changes electrical energy into chemical energy and vice versa.

Its cells contain two sets of porous lead plates, one filled with lead peroxide and the other with spongy lead, immersed in dilute sulfuric acid. When the battery is discharging, the sulfuric acid reacts with the lead peroxide, forming lead sulfate. When the battery is charging, the lead sulfate is changed back into lead peroxide, and sulfuric acid is restored to solution.

You can make an experimental storage battery in a few minutes from two strips of lead (clean them with sandpaper), two matchsticks to hold them apart, rubber bands to bind the assembly together, and a small jar containing 1 part sulfuric acid in 9 parts of water. (Caution: Always pour the acid into the water.)

To charge your improvised battery, connect the plates for five minutes, as shown below at right, to from 2 to 4 dry cells connected in series. During charging, oxygen is released at the positive plate and hydrogen at the negative. Some oxygen unites with the positive plate to form brown lead peroxide. This is visible on the left plate shown in the photograph below at left.

To prove that the chemical change made by electricity can also return electricity, connect a flashlight bulb to the plates of your charged battery. The bulb lights up brightly, as shown in the photograph on the facing page.

 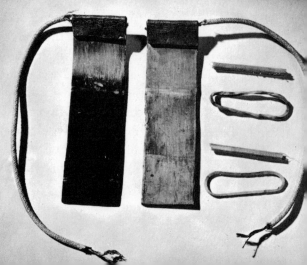

FIRE AND HEAT

Water Starts a Fire!

Most of us think of water as a universal fire extinguisher. Mixed with the wrong substances, however, water may be actually a potent *cause* of fire!

Put water on metallic potassium, for instance, and you start a violent reaction in which hydrogen is released; the great heat from the reaction then sets the hydrogen on fire. Let water fall on powdered sodium peroxide in contact with absorbent cotton and the cotton is oxidized so rapidly that it is soon aflame.

Often water starts a fire by acting as a catalyst—a substance that promotes a reaction between other substances without itself becoming chemically involved. When absolutely dry, certain materials react only feebly or not at all with each other; in the presence of moisture, they react violently.

Here's a spectacular example: In a nonmetallic container, mix thoroughly about ½ thimbleful each of powdered aluminum and iodine crystals. (Don't get the iodine on your hands or on metals, as it is corrosive.) Put the mixture on the center of an asbestos pad, and place this in turn on the bottom of an upturned pie tin.

Under the whole setup spread several thicknesses of newspaper to catch iodine vapors. These vapors are irritating; so make sure there is plenty of ventilation in the room.

When you are all set, make a little depression in the mound of iodine and aluminum and let just one drop of water fall into it. Then stand back!

Within a few seconds the mixture, catalyzed by water, starts to react—a reaction in which the aluminum joins chemically with the iodine. As this reaction speeds up, heat from it produces violet-red iodine vapor which creeps down the sides of the mound. Then suddenly the mixture bursts into flame, accompanied by great volumes of dense smoke.

Light a Fire with a Glass Rod

Do you think you need a flame or a spark to light a fire? In contact with the vapors of such flammable fluids as gasoline, benzene, and ether, red-hot metal will often do the trick. Carbon disulfide vapor can be made to blaze up merely by holding in it a glass rod not much hotter than the boiling point of water!

For proof, pour ½ teaspoonful of carbon disulfide into a can cover, placed on an asbestos mat. (Never pour this liquid in a room with an open flame.) In the next room, heat a glass rod over a match or gas burner. Bring it back, and hold it just above the liquid in the cover. Instantly, the fluid bursts into flame!

The Unburnable Handkerchief

Imagine the consternation of a dinner guest when you dip a handkerchief borrowed from him into a liquid and then set it afire! Imagine, too, his surprise, when you hand it back unharmed!

The secret lies in the liquid, which consists of 2 parts of rubbing alcohol mixed with 1 part of water. Squeeze out the excess liquid and hold the handkerchief with tongs. Hold it away, of course, from any inflammable materials.

What happens when you apply a match to the handkerchief? Only the alcohol burns; the water keeps the temperature of the cloth so low that the handkerchief itself can't catch fire.

Pharaoh's Serpents

When Pharaoh's wise men and sorcerers threw their rods to the ground, says the book of Exodus, the rods changed instantly into serpents. Spurious namesakes of these ancient reptiles have been sold in trick stores for generations: tiny chemical "eggs" which, when lit, grow before your eyes into long writhing "snakes."

The secret behind these modern serpents of Pharaoh is mercuric thiocyanate, a chemical which, on burning, leaves an ash more than 25 times its original volume. With an ounce of this chemical, a pinch of potassium nitrate, and a little mucilage, you can easily make eggs that will produce serpents bigger than any you can buy.

Dissolve the potassium nitrate and a few drops of mucilage in ½ ounce of water. Then—in a glass dish, and using a glass stirring rod —moisten the mercury chemical with this solution until you form a stiff paste. Next mold the paste with your fingers into cones about ¼ inch in diameter and ½ inch high, and set the cones on a glass plate to dry. As the mercury chemical is poisonous, be sure to wash your hands after handling it.

To "hatch" a serpent, set an egg on an asbestos pad or a raised can cover, and light the tip. Instantly, amid fumes and smoke, a snakelike form starts to squirm upward. It continues to grow—apparently from nowhere—until it is several feet long!

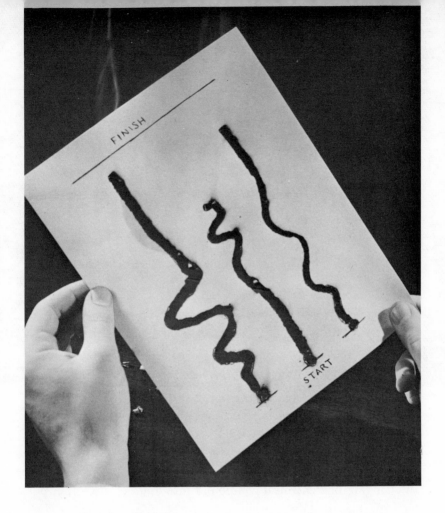

A Chemical Fire Race

You've probably seen "racing sheets" to which several contestants apply the tip of a lighted cigarette—and then cheer on their fiery "horses" as they burn and sputter to the finish line.

These sheets depend upon potassium nitrate, an oxygen-containing chemical used in fuses and gunpowder. Dissolve all the nitrate you can in a teaspoon of warm water. Then, using a glass rod as a pen, draw two or three heavy irregular lines with this solution down the length of a sheet of uncoated paper. With regular ink, mark "start" and "finish" at the ends.

When the lines are dry, each contestant touches a cigarette or match to the start of his chosen line. Slowly and suspensefully, like the spark on a fuse, the fires "race" toward the finish.

97

Light the tip of the orange-colored mound; then turn out lights.

A Magic Volcano

In changing one chemical compound into another, fire often puts on a spectacular show.

Here is an example that always gets applause. To witness it, all you need is a little ammonium bichromate (obtainable at chemical or photographic supply stores), an asbestos mat, and a match.

Place about half a teaspoonful of the orange-colored crystals on the center of the mat, forming them into a mound. Light the tip of this mound and then turn out the room lights.

Viewed in darkness, the burning chemical looks like a miniature volcano, with fiery sparks shooting upward from its crater and lava-like material tumbling down its sides.

The biggest surprise comes when you finally turn on the lights. In place of the original tiny hill of orange crystals, you discover a mountain of green powder! Fire has changed ammonium bichromate into chromium sesquioxide, chromium oxide green—a permanent pigment used in painting and in coloring ceramics!

98

In darkness, the burning chemical looks like a miniature volcano.

When the lights go on, your friends discover a mountain of green!

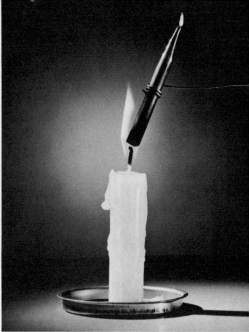

Chemistry in a Candle Flame

In a famous series of lectures delivered nearly a century ago at the British Royal Institution, Michael Faraday proved that the flame of a common candle was really a miniature laboratory in which could be found many fascinating transformations of chemistry.

Although it would take hours to perform all the experiments suggested in Faraday's classic talks, you can easily demonstrate some of the most interesting in a few minutes. The following stunts have been brought up to date for the home scientist.

Do you think a candle flame is hottest at its center? A sheet of paper can help you find out. Hold the paper horizontally and thrust it quickly about ¼ inch above the wick. Remove it as soon as it begins to scorch. If you are quick enough, the flame will form a distinct ring with an unscorched center (photo above, left). Thus it appears to be hollow and fairly cool just above the wick.

In the cool, hollow zone the liquid paraffin that climbs up the candlewick is broken down by the surrounding heat into gases— ethylene, carbon monoxide, acetylene, and hydrogen. The center

of the candle flame may be thought of as the "cracking chamber" of a miniature gas plant.

You can prove the presence of these gases by burning them. Just hold the wide end of the tube from a medicine dropper in the center of the flame and light the jet (photo, right, on facing page).

Ordinarily these gases enter the luminous flame where the carbon monoxide and hydrogen are consumed and the acetylene and ethylene are changed to carbon and hydrogen. In an efficient flame, the latter are then burned in an outer nonluminous part.

When hydrogen burns, it unites with oxygen. So, oddly enough, one by-product of the flame is *water!* You can show this by holding a chilled spoon beside the flame. The spoon will fog, then water droplets may form (photo above, left).

To complete cracking the paraffin and burning the cracked products, the flame must supply sufficient heat. What happens if you cool the flame can be shown by holding a piece of window screening in it. Now unable to burn completely, some of the paraffin oil vapor and black particles of carbon separate from the flame and rise as a column of smoke and soot (photo above, right).

Light That Is Also Heat

Radiant heat is as old as sunlight; it is also as new as the latest infrared broiling ovens, infrared stove elements, glass heating panels, and inexpensive reflector-type bulbs that can warm your body, dry paint, thaw frozen foods, and perform dozens of other specialized heating jobs in home and industry.

Unlike conducted and convected heat, which depend upon physical contact or the circulation of a liquid or gas, radiant heat is a form of visible and invisible light transferred through space by electromagnetic waves. When these waves hit a substance transparent to them—such as space or air—they go right through, as ordinary light goes through clear glass; when they hit a substance that absorbs them they release their energy in the form of heat.

Because radiant heat is really a form of light, it can do many things that other types of heat can't do. For example, it needs no medium to carry it, and air currents can't blow it away. With reflectors you can concentrate its energy and direct it where you want it. Because it can heat foods without heating the surrounding air, you can cook with radiant heat in a cool kitchen.

In semitransparent materials, radiant heat can penetrate the surface. It can thus dry thin paint films from the inside out. For the same reason it can warm your body to a depth without uncomfortably heating the surface.

To show how radiant heat works, try cooking an egg in a glass dish over the rays from a 250-watt reflector-type infrared lamp or an ordinary 300-watt reflector-spot. (See frontispiece.) Because egg substance is heated strongly by infrared rays, while glass is heated feebly, the egg cooks quickly, while your fingers—beyond the reach of the rays—hardly get warm!

As an encore, you can pop corn in a bag made from a cellophane bread wrapper, without damaging the wrapper! The corn absorbs the rays, while the cellophane lets them through. In this case, two lamps—one above and one below, as shown on the next page—work better than one, because the rays cannot penetrate the corn as deeply as they did the egg.

102

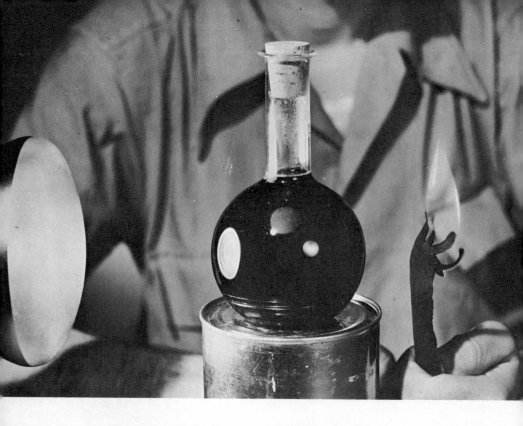

Focused Infrared Lights a Fire

Although radiant heat sometimes includes rays of visible light, its greatest energy is sent forth as infrared—invisible light radiations from beyond the red end of the visible spectrum. One amazing property of invisible infrared is that it can go right through certain substances that stop visible light completely.

To prove this, try the stunt shown above. Fill a 300-milliliter (about 11-ounce) round-bottom flask with carbon tetrachloride made opaque by dissolving in it 3 grams (a little more than $\frac{1}{10}$ ounce) of iodine crystals. Then stand the flask in the beam of a 300-watt reflector-spot lamp.

Although the blackish liquid completely blocks all visible light from the lamp, it acts as a transparent lens to transmit and focus the infrared heat rays. If you doubt it, just move a finger about near the side of the flask opposite the lamp. At the point of focus, you'll move it *fast*. Now hold a piece of frayed black paper at the spot found hottest by your finger. In a few seconds, the paper will burst into flame!

104

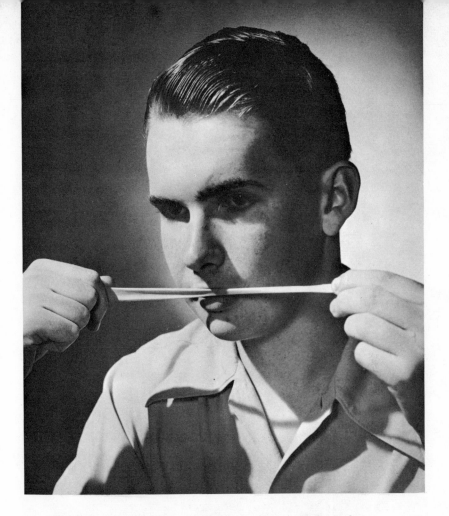

Rubber Heats When Stretched

What puts the bounce in rubber, or causes it to snap back when stretched, is a fascinating subject to science and industry alike. The solution may mean still better synthetic substitutes with the special types of elasticity needed for tires, tubes, balls, and hundreds of other rubber products.

One theory compares the molecules of rubber to those of gases under pressure, and suggests an experiment. Stretch a rubber band quickly to ten times its original length and touch it to your lip. It feels warm. Release it, touch it to your lip again, and it feels cold. The heat generated when the rubber is stretched, scientists claim, is similar to that produced when a gas is compressed, and the cooling to that when pressure in a gas is released.

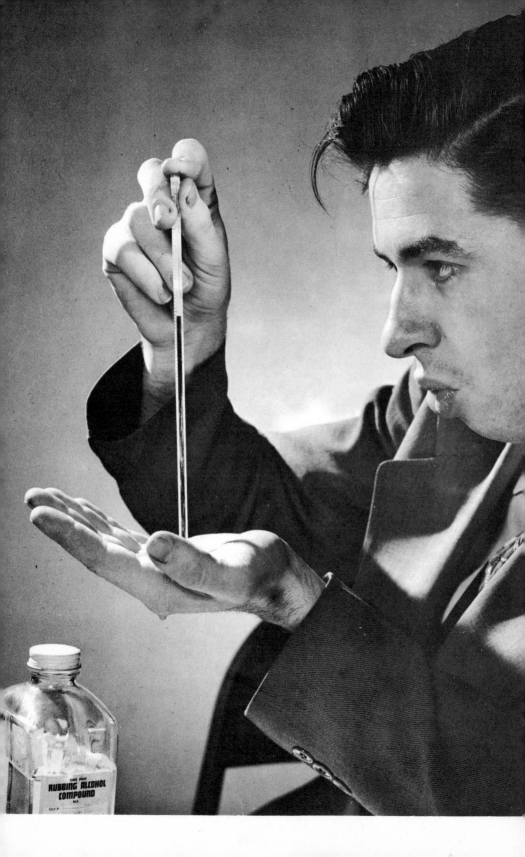

ICE, COLD, AND MAN-MADE RAIN

Evaporation Produces Cold

Whether you have a gleaming new electric or gas refrigerator, an icebox, a primitive evaporative cooler, or an ultramodern gimmick which chills a bottle of liquid refreshment by means of chemicals dissolved in water, the cold-producing principle in it is the same. In each case a solid melts or a liquid evaporates—the heat needed for melting or evaporating being snatched from nearby food and drink, which is thereby cooled.

The common notion that a freezer unit or a chunk of ice *puts cold into your refrigerator* is thus all wrong; the actual job of both ice and unit is *to remove heat!* In a mechanical refrigerator, heat from the box and its contents causes a liquid of low boiling point to evaporate in the cooling coils; the vapor then carries this heat away. In an icebox, heat from the food and box melts the ice and is carried out by the drain water.

Cooling by evaporation is as old as the pyramids. The ancient Egyptians set out porous earthenware jars filled with water. During the night, dry desert breezes evaporated moisture seeping through the pores, chilling the water inside—just as your body becomes chilled when you stand in a breeze while perspiring.

Today, campers and G.I.s cool water by placing it in porous cloth buckets, on the same principle. Country dwellers likewise improvise refrigerators by stretching wet cloths over a box-shaped wooden framework. You experience the same effect when you apply alcohol to cool a fevered skin.

You can demonstrate how evaporation produces cold by standing the bulb of a thermometer in a pool of rubbing alcohol held in your cupped hand. Normal evaporation of the alcohol will steal enough heat from it to lower its temperature several degrees. If you speed up evaporation, by blowing across the alcohol, its temperature will drop as much as 10 degrees.

107

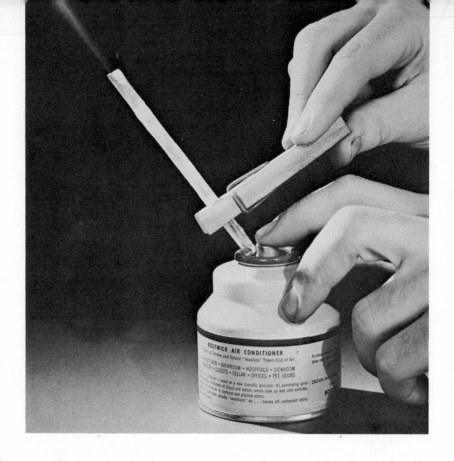

How Your Refrigerator Keeps Frigid

The refrigerator in your kitchen is just a glorified evaporative cooler, with insulated walls to keep out room heat, and an array of pumps, coils, radiators, and control devices to maintain a constant cold inside.

To freeze ice cubes and to keep frozen foods from thawing, a liquid which boils below the freezing point of water must be used in the cooling coils. Commonly used liquids of this type are ammonia, sulfur dioxide, and Freon-12 (dichlorodifluoromethane).

How the boiling and expansion of a liquid with a low boiling point can absorb enough heat to freeze ice cubes may be shown by directing the Freon-propelled spray from a "bug-bomb" through a small metal or glass tube moistened on the outside with water.

Hold the tube with a spring clothespin to keep from warming it or freezing your fingers. In a few seconds, the water will freeze to ice—just as it does in your refrigerator.

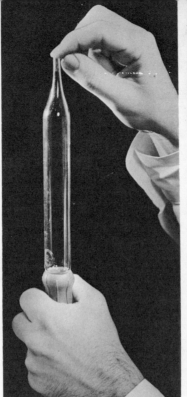

Compression Heats—Expansion Cools

The expanding vapor from an evaporating liquid—by absorbing heat—produces the cooling effect in your electric refrigerator. To change the vapor back into a liquid, the vapor must be first made hotter by squeezing it in a compressor.

How the compression of a gas produces heat, while its expansion produces cold, can be shown visually with a glass meat baster.

Half fill the bulb with water, invert the baster, and draw into it a wisp of smoke from a match to serve as the nuclei for cloud formation (above, left). Then seal the opening with a finger and squeeze the bulb hard (above, center). Any mist that may have been in the tube will disappear instantly. Compression warms the air by crowding it; the warmed air absorbs the moisture droplets.

If you now release the bulb quickly, a dense cloud appears (above, right). Expansion of the air has cooled it, and in so doing has squeezed out droplets of excess moisture.

109

A Cut Ice Cube Remains Whole

Would you believe you could cut through an ice cube without dividing it? The photograph above shows how to perform this feat.

Provide handles at the ends of an 8-inch length of thin wire by twisting each end around the middle of a pencil. Place an ice cube on top of a bottle. Then straddle the cube with the wire and bear down hard on the pencils.

Within a minute or so the wire will cut its way completely through the cube and come out the bottom. The ice cube, however, will still be whole and as solid as before you started!

How is this possible? Pressure causes the ice directly under the wire to melt. In melting, this ice steals heat from the ice surrounding it. The latter, colder ice refreezes the water after the wire has passed through.

Why Lakes Freeze from the Top Down

Every householder who has had his pipes burst in cold weather knows that water expands when it freezes. Few realize, however, that water, unlike any other liquid, starts to expand even before it reaches the freezing point. It is this peculiarity of water that causes ice to form on top of lakes before the bottom. Like other liquids, water at high temperatures contracts as it cools. At 4 degrees centigrade (about 39 degrees Fahrenheit), however, this contraction stops and water starts to expand again.

You can prove the expansion of water with the setup above. Fill a small bottle with colored water, stop it with a cork having a thin glass tube through it, and press in the cork until the water rises a few inches in the tube. Mark this point on a scale fastened to the tube and bury the bottle in a tumbler of cracked ice and salt. As the water cools, it goes down to a final low point shown in the center photograph. Further cooling causes it to rise again.

111

How "Seeding" Starts Snow and Rain

According to the men who make rain and snow by "seeding" the clouds, raindrops and snowflakes begin as minute ice crystals in a cloud whose temperature is below freezing. Additional moisture freezes around these ice crystals and causes them to grow until they are heavy enough to fall. They finally reach the earth as snow or rain, depending on the temperature of the lower air.

If the cloud is cold enough (below −31 degrees Fahrenheit) the tiny ice-crystal nuclei will form spontaneously. If it isn't, the crystals won't form unless there are enough suitable dusts in the cloud to give them a start.

The secret of the rainmakers is to supply *artificial nuclei* to clouds that can't produce their own. They usually do this either by freezing water droplets directly, with the help of pellets of dry ice, or by peppering supercooled clouds with microscopic particles of silver iodide around which crystals can form.

EASTMAN KODAK COMPANY

How "seeds" or nuclei start the formation of crystals can be shown more readily with a supersaturated solution than with a supercooled cloud.

Heat gently a spoonful of crystals of ordinary photographer's "hypo" (sodium thiosulfate) in a spoon. After the crystals have completely melted in their own water, carefully scrape off any dirt or scum from the surface of the resulting liquid with a bit of paper. Then prop up the spoon so the liquid can cool undisturbed.

Oddly enough (unless the liquid is jarred or contaminated), mere cooling will not cause the hypo to "freeze" back into its original crystalline form (photograph on the opposite page). If, however, you drop into the liquid a few specks of a broken-up hypo crystal, these act as seeds, and crystallization thenceforth takes place rapidly. Within a few seconds, all the liquid will once more be transformed into solid hypo (photograph above).

Tiny ice seeds, by means of a similar triggering action, cause whole supercooled clouds to turn into snow.

For insulation, wrap a folded bath towel around the outer can, tucking the excess under it.

Place the small can inside the large one and pack the space between with ice and salt.

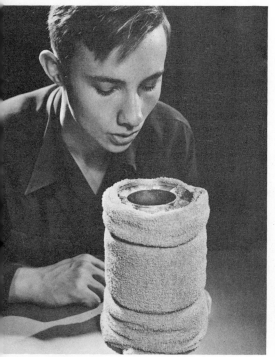

To make a cloud, breathe into the small can. Your breath will change into a visible vapor.

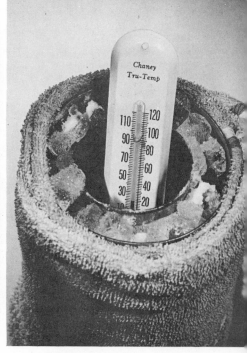

Although the temperature soon drops below freezing, vapor in the small can does not freeze.

How to Supercool a Cloud

You don't have to drop dry ice from an airplane or send up silver iodide from the ground to find out how cloud-seeding works. With a chunk of dry ice from a package of ice cream, plus tin cans, ice cubes, a towel, and the other easily obtained items shown above, you can duplicate this trick of the rainmakers in your kitchen.

The only apparatus you need is a chamber to cool a miniature cloud to a temperature below freezing. You can make the one described here at no cost, and can operate it for more than an hour with less than two trays of ice cubes from your refrigerator.

Details of construction are shown on the opposite page. To hold the ice use a tall 46-ounce fruit juice can; for the chamber itself use a tall 12-ounce can. So you can see the ice crystals better, coat the inside of the chamber with flat black paint.

The cooling mixture between the cans consists of 3 parts of cracked ice and 1 part of salt (either rock salt or table salt). After insulating the outer can with the towel, put 2 inches of cracked ice in it and add salt. Then insert the small can, and pack ice and salt mixture around it right up to the top.

To make a cloud, breathe into the cold chamber. The moisture from your breath will instantly condense into microscopic water droplets. Although this cloud soon becomes many degrees below freezing, its droplets—like the droplets in a supercooled cloud in the sky—do not freeze.

Make a Snowstorm in Your Kitchen

To work your cloud-seeding magic, pick up your piece of dry ice (insulated from your fingers with several thicknesses of paper or cloth) and scrape a few grains off it with a nail, letting them fall into the cloud.

Then shine a flashlight into the chamber and watch carefully. In a few moments you will see a myriad of tiny ice crystals sparkling among the droplets. These tiny crystals are like the "diamond dust" that makes up feathery cirrus clouds and falls from the sky on cold clear days in the mountains. They are also identical to the seeds or sublimation nuclei which often start snowstorms.

To make the seeds grow, breathe again into the chamber—this time, *gently,* to avoid melting the crystals. The new moisture will quickly freeze around the crystals. If you repeat this operation a few times, several minutes apart, the crystals may become large enough to fall to the bottom as tiny flakes of snow.

Because your cloud is so small, the seeding efficiency of the dry ice is low. In a real cloud, a single cubic inch of dry ice could conceivably trigger at least 20,000,000 tons of snow!

Under a flashlight, tiny ice crystals sparkle in the cloud made by your breath. They are like the "seeds" which start snowstorms.

LIGHT—VISIBLE AND INVISIBLE

Why Water Seems Shallower Than It Is

Have you ever plunged into water that looked chest-deep, only to discover it was really over your head? Then you have been fooled by light waves that have been bent from their normal paths!

You can see how this illusion works by looking straight down into a tumbler of water. Although your reason tells you that it can't be so, the bottom of the glass looks as if it were closer to your eyes than the table on which it stands!

Why? Because light waves from the bottom of the glass are bent out of shape as they pass upward into the air through the surface of the water. As a result, they seem to originate from a point higher than the actual bottom of the glass.

The amount the light waves are bent, and hence the height at which the phantom bottom appears above the real bottom, depends upon the relationship between the speed of light in air and the speed of light in water.

You can roughly determine this relationship by touching the tip of a pencil to the outside of the glass at the point where the bottom appears to be (a stirring rod, placed diagonally in the glass, may help you locate this point) and then comparing the height of the water below the pencil with that above. As measurements by more elaborate means have established the fact that light travels about three-fourths as fast in water as in air, the pencil will come to rest about three-fourths of the way between the surface of the water and the bottom.

The relative speed of light through other transparent liquids can be measured by substituting these liquids for water and then repeating your experiment. No common liquid will appear deeper than water. As light travels more slowly through benzene, mineral oil, acetone, and carbon tetrachloride, however, these substances will all appear shallower than water.

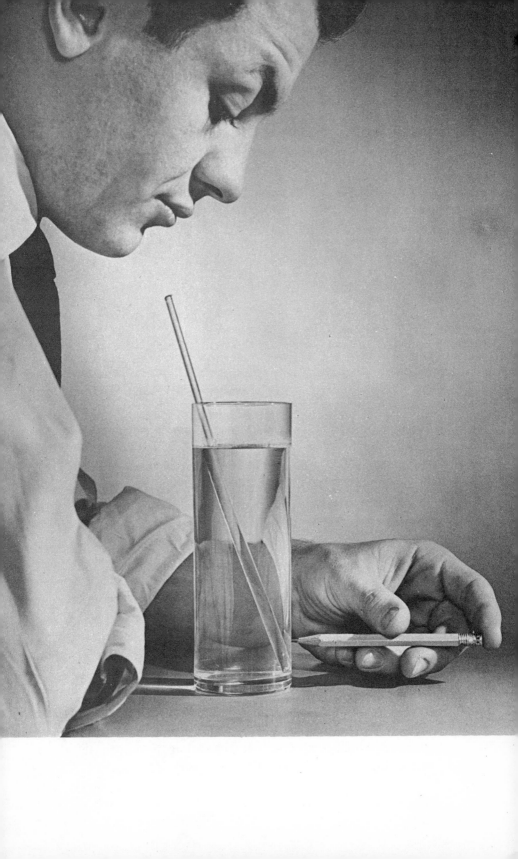

Where Does the Color Go?

Rubies are red; emeralds are green. But *powdered* rubies and emeralds are *white!*

The color of transparent substances, such as gem stones, glass, plastics, and crystalline chemicals is due to the fact that these substances partly transmit and partly reflect the color observed, and absorb all other colors. To display its normal color, however, the substance must be in pieces that are large compared with the minute wave lengths of light.

You can demonstrate this trick of light with a crystal of copper sulfate or a bit of colored glass. In its original form, the copper sulfate is deep blue. (Above, left.) But powder the crystal with a hammer and the color disappears! (Above, right.)

Where does the color go? It is still in the powdered crystal, but you can't see it because light striking the powder is scattered in all directions from the surfaces of the tiny particles.

You can show that the color has not really left the substance by moistening the powdered glass or chemical with a little water. The water helps the light to penetrate by blending the individual surfaces of the powder particles, and the color partly returns.

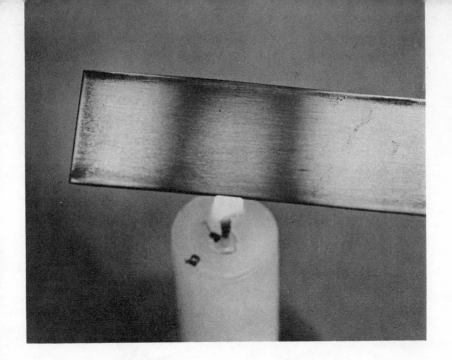

Rainbows on Your Pots and Pans

Do you imagine that the rainbow colors which appear mysteriously on overheated steel pots and pans are due to pigments deposited by the flame? Not at all! Like the colors of oil on wet pavements, soap bubbles, and iridescent glass, they are conjured up from colorless transparent surface films by a trick of light!

The film on your pots consists of a coating of iron oxide only a few millionths of an inch thick. When white light hits this coating, part of the light is reflected from the upper surface and part from the lower. As the two paths are not of equal length, certain light waves get out of step and so cancel each other.

The result? If the film is of uniform thickness, the surface takes on a color made up of all the remaining colors in the spectrum! If the film varies in thickness, the surface shows a rainbow!

To see how such colors are made, hold a thin strip of steel over a candle flame. As the strip heats (and a thickening film forms on it), it magically changes color—first yellow and brown, then red, purple, and blue! Finally, the part of the strip over the flame becomes so hot (and the film so thick) that the colors retreat toward the ends, leaving the hot spot again colorless!

121

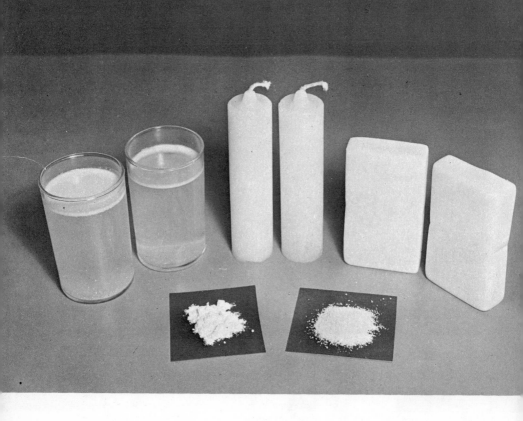

Invisible Light Makes Things Brighter

What is the secret of the dazzling new paints and dyes that shine three or four times brighter than ordinary colors? How does the "sunshine" ingredient in soaps and washing powders make clothes whiter than they can be bleached? What enables fluorescent lamps to give more light per watt than incandescent bulbs?

The answer to each of these questions is the same. Special *fluorescent* chemical compounds in the paints, dyes, and detergents, and on the glass of the light tubes, absorb short invisible light waves from beyond the violet end of the spectrum and transform them into longer waves which you can see as color.

Ordinarily you see an object as red because the object reflects red radiations from the light around it and absorbs all the other colors of the spectrum. Fluorescent red reflects these radiations too, but it also changes part of the invisible ultraviolet into red, thus augmenting its brilliance. The new optical bleaches now

included in many soaps and detergents help combat the yellowing of white goods by shining with an intense blue fluorescence. Fluorescent lamps produce more light for your money because they efficiently convert electricity into invisible ultraviolet, and then change this "black light" into visible light of the color desired.

How ultraviolet light makes everyday materials shine in the dark can be shown with the help of a special purple-glass incandescent bulb now available. Although this bulb gives almost no visible light, its rays cause your teeth, eyes, and fingernails to glow weirdly; fluorescent pigments and dyes shine fiercely under it; many colored objects change color completely.

Objects which look exactly alike under ordinary light often become spectacularly different under ultraviolet. Some soaps and detergent powders, for instance, fluoresce; others do not. Paraffin candles fluoresce; tallow candles do not. How some common materials change in appearance when viewed under white and ultraviolet light is shown in the photographs on these pages.

123

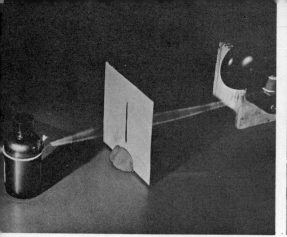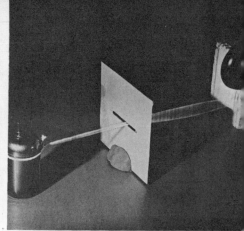

One-way Light

How do polarizing sunglasses protect your eyes from glare at the beach? Why does a polarizing visor on your car improve your driving vision? How may polarizing screens, applied to the headlights and windshields of all cars, make night driving safer?

All these useful devices depend upon *polarized* or "one way" light. Ordinary light vibrates in every possible direction in the plane perpendicular to the line in which the light is traveling. Polarized light vibrates in this same plane, but in only one direction.

Every-way light may be changed into one-way light by several means. One is to pass it through a polarizing filter—a grille consisting of microscopic crystals lined up in one direction in transparent plastic. Only light vibrating in a line parallel to them can get past the crystalline bars. The one-way light that gets through will be stopped completely if it encounters a second filter with its bars turned at right angles to those in the first.

Perhaps the mechanical analogy shown above will help you understand how polarized light works. A string, tied at one end to the clapper of an electric bell and at the other to a fixed support, will be vibrated *up and down* by the bell clapper, and can be likened to light that has been polarized by passing through a single filter. Provide another filter by passing the string through a narrow slit in a square of cardboard. If the slot in the cardboard is arranged in the direction of the vibration, the wave goes through. If the slot is turned at right angles to the vibration, however, the vibration is stopped.

With the help of a flashlight and two pairs of polarizing sunglasses (or two polarizing filters of any kind) you can demonstrate polarization using light itself.

First hold a lens of one of the glasses in front of the light. Although the light that shines through looks just like ordinary light (above, left), it is really polarized. If you doubt it, rotate a lens of the second pair of glasses in front of and parallel with the first lens. The light coming through the second lens dims and brightens as the relationship between the grilles in the two lenses changes. When the lenses are exactly at right angles (above, right) the light will be blacked out completely!

It has been proposed that this principle be used to control glare from car headlights. Polarizing screens, with their crystals aligned diagonally, would be placed over the lamps. Another screen, with its crystals aligned in the same direction, would go on the windshield.

When two cars so equipped faced each other, the polarizing screen on your windshield and those on the lamps of the other car would cross at right angles. The other driver's headlights would appear dim, although you could still see the highway perfectly.

125

Light reflected ... often polari... ...rfaces ...is ...tent if the li... ...reatest ex- ...bout 35°.

How Polarizing Glasses Reduce Glare

Light also becomes polarized by reflection at certain angles from a smooth nonmetallic surface. The glare reflected from water, an automobile highway, or the glossy page of a book—when the sun or other illumination is above and ahead of you—is thus largely made up of light vibrating in a single direction. By providing yourself with polarizing sunglasses or a car visor with crystals lined up in the opposite direction this glare can easily be stopped.

A polarizing filter, placed over your camera lens and properly aligned, can similarly reduce glare and reflections bounced off show windows, polished wood or plastic table tops, shiny textiles, and other nonmetal objects. Metals, on the other hand (evidently because of their different molecular structure), do not polarize light reflected from them. Therefore, glare from mirrors, silverware,

126

Light reflected from nonmetallic surfaces is often polarized. This occurs to the greatest extent if the light hits and rebounds at about 35°.

coins, and other metallic objects cannot be dimmed by a polarizing screen.

How polarizing glasses or filters can cut glare from wood and paper, yet not from metal, can be shown simply.

Place a smooth picture on a polished table top, put a coin on the picture, and then view all three by the light of a desk lamp set up just above and beyond them. When the objects and the lamp are arranged thus, reflected glare obliterates all detail from the picture and table, and shines dazzlingly from the coin (as shown in the photograph on the opposite page).

Now—without changing anything—look at this arrangement through your polarizing glasses (or through a polarizing filter rotated until the glare is at its minimum). Glare has disappeared from the table, you can see the picture clearly—yet the coin looks just the same! (Photograph above.)

127

SEEING IS DECEIVING

Want to See a Ghost?

Next time you spot a ghost, don't be frightened. Yet don't be too sure, either, that what you see is merely a creature of your imagination! For everyone is constantly haunted by real ghosts—white, black, and colored *afterimages* conjured up by the retina of the eye after it has been overstimulated by light.

The best way to become acquainted with these afterimage specters is to make one to order. To do so, just hold this page under a strong light and stare fixedly at the head below for about half a minute. Then look away toward a dimly lit blank wall. Within seconds you will see a white face with black eyes and nose, and teeth outlined in black, seemingly projected against the wall!

For the next few minutes, this ghost will haunt you wherever you look. You won't be able to dispel it even by closing your eyes!

Psychologists tell us that such ghosts are produced by retinal fatigue. When you stare at the head under a strong light, the light

reflected from the white eyes, nose, and outline, tires the area of the retina on which it falls. This tired area responds more feebly when you shift your gaze. As a result, you see an image in which black is white and white is black.

Such afterimages might explain the apparitions some persons see hovering over their beds or flitting through graveyards. After seeing a chair silhouetted against a lamp, or a tombstone against the moon, you might later see a filmy phantom which might resemble a ghost.

128

See through Your Hand!

When you say, "I can't believe my eyes!" you are uttering more truth than you may think. Although human eyes usually do an amazingly good job, they can sometimes trick you into thinking you see things you actually don't see.

Here is an example. Roll a sheet of paper into a tube about an inch in diameter. Look through this tube with your left eye, and at your hand, held beside the tube, with the right eye. Although you know it can't be true, a hole appears right in the middle of your hand, through which you can see objects beyond it!

What you witness is of course an illusion. Because your two eyes normally produce a single image, your mind automatically superimposes the image seen by one eye upon that seen by the other.

The Phantom Frankfurter

Bring your index fingers together about a foot and a half in front of you. If you focus your eyes on the tips of the fingers, the fingers appear normal. Focus your eyes on a distant wall, however, and an amazing transformation takes place: a short, two-ended finger, resembling a cocktail frankfurter, appears between your finger tips! Separate your fingers slightly and this miniature hot dog remains suspended in mid-air!

Whence comes this gratuitous tidbit? It is a phantom conjured up by your eyes when you try to make them do two things at once. When you look past your nearby fingers each eye makes a separate, side-by-side image of them. If you hold your fingers just right, these images overlap at the center to form an extra shape.

Every Eye Has a Blind Spot

Even though your vision is otherwise perfect, in each of your eyes you have one spot which is totally blind. If you doubt it, close your left eye and stare with your right at the dot in the photograph above. Then—starting at a distance of about a foot—move the book slowly toward you. When you reach a certain distance (probably between 10 and 11 inches) the head of the young man at the right of the dot will suddenly disappear!

What happens to him? His image falls on the little spot on your retina where the optic nerve enters the eyeball. This spot, which is about $\frac{1}{12}$ inch in diameter and 15 degrees off center in the direction of your nose, is completely insensitive to light.

The visual area affected by the blind spot increases with the distance. At 7 feet, for example, a person's whole face can vanish. Simply place the person against a wall, close your left eye, and sight with your right eye at a point about 20 inches from his right cheek. At 60 feet, a 6-foot man can be blanked out.

If you have two good eyes, you do not ordinarily notice the blind spots because the field of vision blanked out by the spot in one eye is covered by a sensitive spot in the other eye.

Are You Right-eyed or Left-eyed?

Although you may never have noticed it, you are right-eyed or left-eyed just as definitely as you are right-handed or left-handed. In all your seeing, one eye leads and the other eye follows.

To find out which eye is dominant, first point at a distant object with both eyes open, as shown above. Then close your right eye. If your finger seems to jump sharply to the right, you are right-eyed. If it doesn't move, you are left-eyed.

You can aim a rifle better, and see better through a telescope or microscope, if you remember to use your dominant eye.

A Cardboard Disk Stops Motion

By looking through slits in a device which you can conjure up in a minute, a whirling electric fan will seem to stand still, a clapper will ring a bell while apparently not moving, alternating current will appear to stop alternating!

To make this motion-freezing *stroboscope*, first cut two slits, about $\frac{1}{16}$ inch wide and 1 inch long, on opposite sides of a 6-inch disk of cardboard. By means of the screw eye, attach this disk to the spindle described on page 35. Then insert the spindle in a chuck of your electric mixer (photograph below, left).

To use it, look through the slits toward a revolving or vibrating object, and carefully adjust the speed of the mixer so that one slit passes your eye every time the object makes a complete revolution or vibration. The object will seem to stand still!

Engineers use more elaborate stroboscopes to detect flaws in rapidly moving machinery. Your simple instrument can show how.

Mount a "broken gear," cut from cardboard, on an electric drill (photo below, right). Then spin the gear and observe it as shown at the top of the next page. When the speed of your mixer is just right, the broken tooth will be visible!

To stop the fluctuations of alternating current, look at a fluorescent light through the rotating slit (lower photograph on next page). Although the light ordinarily seems continuous, it slowly dims and brightens when seen through the stroboscope. By careful adjustment of the mixer speed, you can make the lamp appear continuously dim or continuously bright.

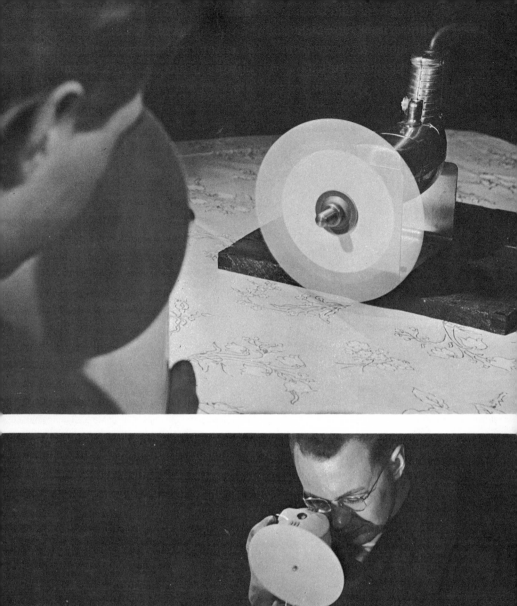
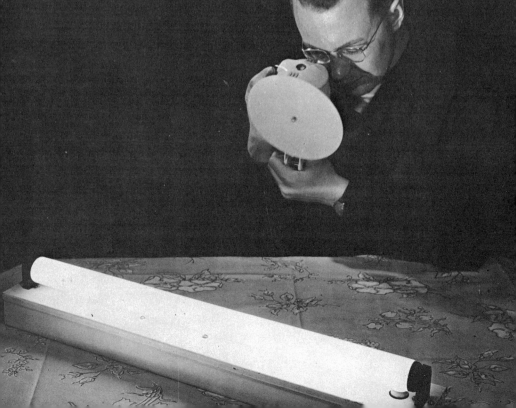

How to See Colors That Aren't There

Don't try to select neckties or to interpret traffic lights while looking through the rotating disk shown above. For—among other
topsy-turvy color transformations—it makes you see red as green
and white as black!

Besides your kitchen mixer, all the equipment you need to make
this baffling device is a disk of white cardboard about 7 inches in
diameter. Blacken half of the disk and cut a segment from one edge,

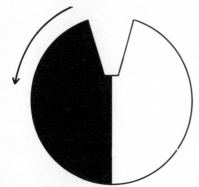

as shown at the left. Attach it to the pencil spindle and insert the spindle in the
mixer chuck that rotates counterclock-
wise. Now look at a small, colored light
through the aperture in the edge of the
disk, while revolving the disk slowly
under a moderately strong white light.
Instead of seeing its proper color, you

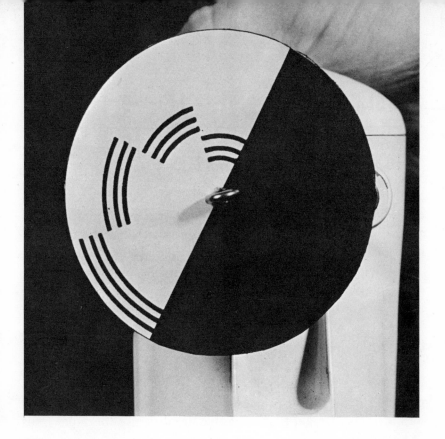

see the light from the little bulb as its complementary! Like the ghost at the beginning of this chapter, this illusion is caused by retinal fatigue. Your eye tires to the color it sees through the aperture, and so projects an image of complementary color on the white section of the disk. As the white section is wider than the aperture, the complementary color predominates.

Your mixer can help you perform still another mystifying trick of vision. This time cut a disk of white cardboard 4 inches in diameter. Blacken half of it as before and draw sections of circles on the other half, as shown above.

If you rotate this disk slowly under strong white light, the arcs of black ink seem to change magically to circles of four different colors! Change the direction of rotation and the colors appear again, but in reverse sequence!

What produces these colors that really aren't there? No one definitely knows. The final answer will probably relate the effect to the rate of growth and decay of color sensations in the eye and mind, a subject which thus far is imperfectly understood.

COSMIC RAYS AND ATOMIC ENERGY

How to See Cosmic Rays at Home

With nothing but a peanut-butter jar, a chunk of dry ice, and several odds and ends picked up around the house, you can easily build a workable cloud chamber in which you can witness the effects of some of the most talked-of wonders of the universe.

Mysterious cosmic rays bombarding the earth's atmosphere from outside space, atomic explosions from radioactive ores, particles thrown off by disintegrating atoms from the radium dial of a watch —all sorts of radiations leave fascinating cloud trails as they streak through this homemade "atomic showcase."

The secret of any cloud chamber is an atmosphere supersaturated with the vapor of water or alcohol. As atomic radiations dart through this vapor, they cause molecules in their path to condense —thus leaving behind trails of visible droplets, like the vapor trails of high-flying aircraft.

In the original cloud chamber—invented in 1911 by the British atom pioneer C. T. R. Wilson, and still an important research tool —the supersaturated atmosphere required is produced by suddenly cooling moist air in the chamber, by withdrawing a piston. As the supersaturated condition lasts only a few seconds, the piston must be withdrawn each time new trails are to be observed.

The device described here is a simplified version of a new type of cloud chamber which has no moving parts and operates continuously. Instead of using a piston, warm alcohol vapor is caused to diffuse downward through a layer of air chilled by dry ice. At some point between the top and bottom of the chamber, the vapor becomes cool enough to produce a state of supersaturation.

All the materials you need for the cloud chamber proper are shown at the bottom of the opposite page. Details for assembling them are given on the two pages that follow. A home movie or slide projector, aimed as shown above, will provide suitable light.

To use your cloud chamber, warm the inverted bottom for a minute with your hand. Then watch closely. In a moment you should see straight shafts and zigzags of vapor. These are trails of cosmic rays, mighty forces let loose from outside our local world. To see the vaporous signatures of beta and gamma rays from exploding radium, just hold a luminous watch dial near the jar.

Cement weatherstrip around the inside of the jar next to the bottom. Use rubber cement.

Cement black velvet strip around the inside of the jar mouth. Black will help you see the rays.

A Cloud Chamber from a Jar

To make your cloud chamber, choose a squat, wide-mouthed jar such as peanut butter and cake frosting often come in—preferably one with a rubber ring in the cap. Using rubber cement, fasten a piece of felt weather strip around the inside of the jar, at the bottom. This is to retain the alcohol. To provide a dark background for observing, cement similarly a disk of black velvet to the inside of the cap, and a strip of this material, ¾ inch wide, around the inside of the jar, at the mouth.

To support the cloud chamber, and make the dry ice last longer, make a base by filling a coffee can with absorbent cotton; imbed the dry ice in this, leaving only its top face exposed.

Any of the common alcohols (ethyl, methyl, or propyl) will provide a suitable vapor. If the cloud chamber suddenly stops working, all the alcohol has probably evaporated from the weather strip and condensed in the cap. Just turn the jar over to rewet the strip, and then invert it again. Your vapor trails will reappear.

Cement a disk of black velvet to the underside of the jar cap to complete the dark background.

Pour in enough alcohol to saturate the felt strip and leave about ⅛ inch in the bottom of jar.

Close cover, invert jar, and rest it on a slab of dry ice imbedded in cotton in the base.

Shine beam of slide projector through jar and you'll see cloud trails of cosmic rays.

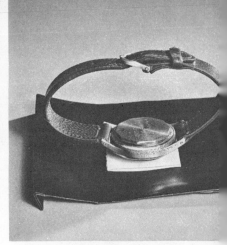

Atomic Energy Makes an X-ray Photo

Using atomic rays shot out from the radium-coated numbers on your wrist-watch dial you can easily make an X-ray photograph. At the same time you can duplicate the "lucky accident" which started off the whole new science of nuclear physics and atomic energy.

Until 1896, atoms (the "indivisible") were supposed to be the smallest possible units of matter. In that year the French physicist Henri Becquerel made a startling discovery. Between experiments with phosphorescent materials he left several photographic plates, wrapped in black paper, next to some salts of uranium in a dark drawer. Upon developing the plates a few days later Becquerel found to his amazement that the plates had become fogged!

Further investigation by this scientist and others soon revealed that the fogging was caused by radiations thrown off by *exploding atoms*. As each atom blew up, it sent out particles and rays at such high speeds that some of them could go right through paper and even metals. The most penetrating of these radiations, called *gamma rays*, were similar to X rays, but of shorter wave length.

Here was man's first evidence that the atom, which for more than two thousand years had been considered the basic building block of the universe, must itself be made up of smaller blocks. Quite by accident, Becquerel had stumbled upon one of the greatest discoveries in the whole history of science!

142

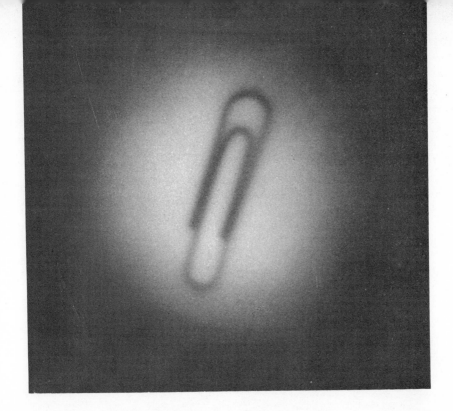

Radium, found in 1898 by Pierre and Marie Curie, is about two million times as radioactive as uranium. The minute quantity of radium on your watch dial, therefore, should penetrate paper even better than Becquerel's original material.

To make your X-ray photograph, all you need are the items shown at the top of the facing page, plus a piece of photographic film about 2 inches square. Put the film, emulsion side up, into a black paper envelope, or wrap it well in black paper. (Do either in a totally dark room.) On top of the wrapped film place a paper clip sandwiched between the two halves of a strip of cardboard bent double. Place the watch, face down, on top of the sandwich.

After an exposure of from 10 hours to several days (depending upon the speed of the film) develop the film. You should have a clear radiograph of the clip, as shown above, made by atomic rays!

Film badge *dosimeters*, worn by workers in atomic plants, work on the same principle. Special film is enclosed in a light-tight envelope and placed in the badge. At fixed intervals the film is developed. The density of the fog on the film indicates the amount of radiation to which the wearer has been exposed.

143

Your Electroscope Detects Radiation

If you think you've discovered uranium in your back yard, don't rush out and buy a Geiger counter until you've made a test with your homemade electroscope (pages 76 and 77).

To test ore for radioactivity, first charge the electroscope by rubbing a hard rubber comb on wool and drawing it over the knob. Then carefully remove the cover, put the suspected sample into the jar, and replace the cover. If the air is dry and the ore is *not* radioactive, the electroscope should hold its charge as much as a day or more. If it loses its charge in less than an hour, the ore is probably radioactive.

144

To discharge your electroscope by radiation in a matter of seconds, merely hold the radium dial of a clock or watch (with its crystal removed to permit the passage of the more energetic though less penetrating alpha rays) several inches from the knob. The electroscope leaves will collapse before your eyes.

Atomic radiations discharge the electroscope by *ionizing* the air. When atomic rays speed through air they knock off electrons from atoms and molecules in their path. Each atom that loses an electron becomes positively charged. Likewise, every whole atom that picks up a free electron becomes negatively charged.

These charged atoms are called *ions*, or "wanderers." Ions of a charge opposite to that on the electroscope give to or take electrons from the latter charge, and so neutralize it.

145

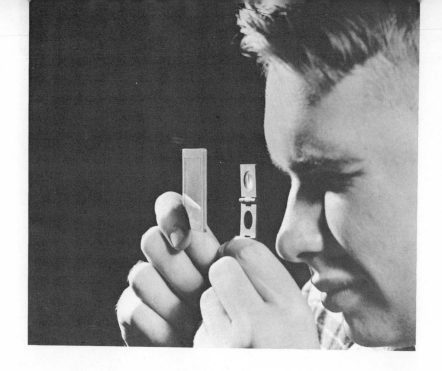

Pocket Viewer Shows Atomic Explosions

No man has ever seen an individual atom. By looking into the *spinthariscope*, or "spark-viewer," of Sir William Crookes, however, he can see vividly what happens when individual atoms explode.

In this fascinating device—invented in 1903 and still widely used —a speck of a radium salt is supported near a screen coated with phosphorescent zinc sulfide. Each time a radium atom disintegrates it shoots out an alpha particle at the rate of 10,000 miles a second. When this alpha particle smashes into a zinc sulfide molecule on the screen the collision produces a flash of light.

With a few grains of radium paint from a discarded clock dial, a little phosphorescent zinc sulfide (from a chemical supply house), two 2- by 2-inch glass plates, and a short-focus magnifier, you can make an even more spectacular version of Crookes's invention.

The photographs on the opposite page show you how. First scrape the paint from a single number onto a piece of paper. (Although the amount of radium in the paint is minute, be careful with it: don't scatter it, and wash off any you may get on your hands.) Next mix this paint with about a gram of the zinc sulfide.

Put the mixture into a small vial and cover the mouth of the vial with a piece of gauze, holding it in place with tape. Then sprinkle the mixture onto a 2 by 2 square of black paper. Finally sandwich the radium-coated paper between the two glass plates and bind the edges of the sandwich with tape as you would a lantern slide. As phosphorescent zinc sulfide glows after being exposed to light, the plates should be kept wrapped in black paper, or stored in an opaque envelope, when not being used.

To witness the spectacle your spinthariscope offers, view the slide with a magnifier (3 to 10 times magnification) in a dark room after your eyes have become adapted to the darkness. Each of the thousands of tiny flashes you see sparkling like twinkling stars against the black background is the signal flare of an atomic bullet that has hit its mark!

147

CHEMICAL MAGIC

Chemicals with a Backbone of Sand

Until about 1948, you knew the silicones chiefly by reputation. Today, however, in dozens of new products for the homeowner, car owner, and sportsman, you have a chance to meet these amazing compounds face to face.

New polishes for furniture contain silicone oils which leave a hard protective film that sheds water and helps prevent the adherence of dust and dirt. Applied to both painted and chrome automobile surfaces, silicone car polishes form a tough, invisible coating that protects against salt air, moisture, and smog.

A thin film of silicone grease, applied to pots and pans merely by rubbing it on, prevents food from sticking. Golf balls with silicone centers are said to drive farther. Fishing lines and flies, treated with silicones, float better and last longer.

Outwardly, the silicones look for all the world like oils, greases, resins, and substitutes for rubber with which you are familiar. Tests in use, however, reveal remarkable differences.

One outstanding trait of the silicones is their ability to repel

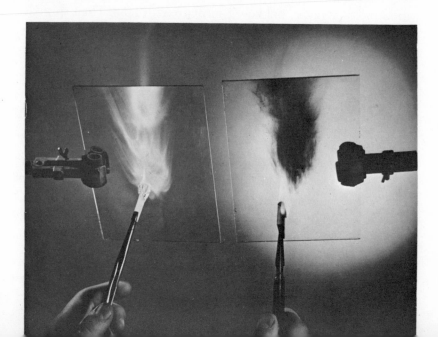

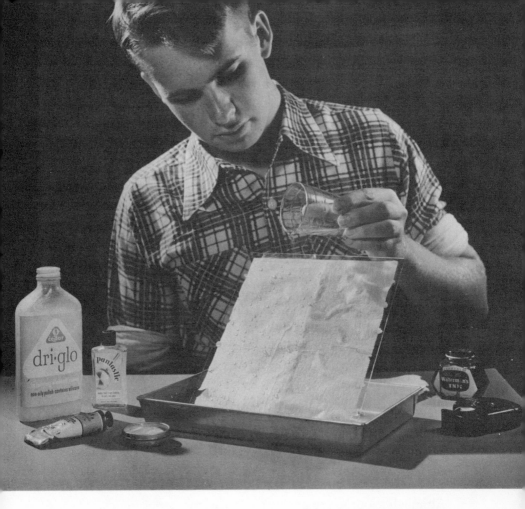

water. Another—thanks to a "backbone" of silica—is their ability to stand up against heat that would break down comparable organic materials and cold that would freeze them.

To demonstrate convincingly the basic difference between silicones and their organic counterparts, just burn a bit of silicone rubber (silicone stopcock grease will do) alongside a similar bit of ordinary rubber—catching the smoke from each on a sheet of glass. From the ordinary rubber comes the black soot of unburned carbon. From the silicone rubber comes the white vapor of silicon oxide—finely divided white sand!

To show how silicones repel water, rub Dri-Glo, or similar silicone furniture polish, on half of a paper towel. Then support the towel as shown above and pour water down it. The water rolls off the silicone-treated half, while it soaks the other.

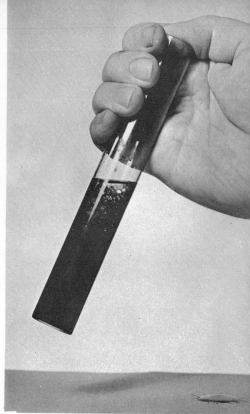

This Filter Separates Oil from Water

Although clothing treated with a silicone water repellent sheds water like a duck's back, it lets air and water vapor through as if it were a sieve. That's why water-*repellent* clothing is more comfortable than the water*proof* variety, such as plastic or rubber. The latter not only keeps out water, but prevents air circulation and traps perspiration.

That it is possible for a material to shed water and still be porous to other fluids can be proved graphically. Cut a disk 6 inches in diameter from a paper towel, and give each side two coats of Dri-Glo. Then fold this disk in quarters and place it in a funnel.

Next, pour equal parts of benzine and water colored with ink into a small bottle. Shake this thoroughly and then pour the mixture into your filter, supported over another bottle.

In a matter of seconds, the clear benzine starts trickling through, while the colored water remains in the filter (right).

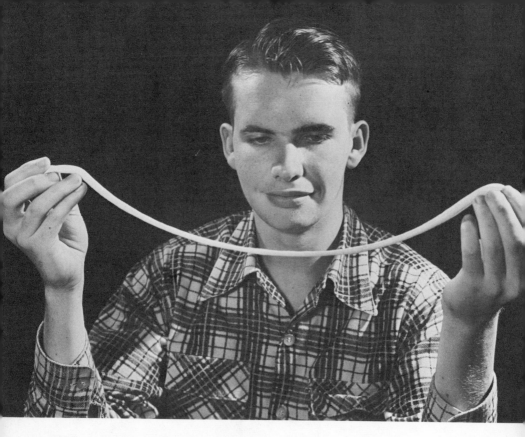

Pull slowly, and this strangest of silicones stretches like taffy.

Putty That Bounces

Strangest among the silicones is "bouncing putty." Squeeze this odd material in your fingers and it shapes up like modeling clay; pull it slowly and it stretches like taffy; hit it a swift blow with a hammer and it shatters like glass; throw it against a hard surface and it bounces like a ball!

Bouncing putty was discovered almost accidentally by scientists who were developing silicone rubber, resins, oils, and greases. Its curious properties delighted the eyes of layman and chemist alike. But for the next several years the only practical use that was found for it was in physiotherapy, as a kneading material to help strengthen hands that were crippled.

Then experts of a big rubber company tried putting a pellet of bouncing putty in the center of golf balls. One unique trait of the putty, they knew, was that it would rebound faster and higher than

Drop a ball of this putty, and it
bounces better than rubber.

Smack it with a hammer, and it
will shatter like glass!

natural rubber. Results indicated that the new center brought greater distance and improved the "click" and "feel" of the ball. Today, all this company's top grade balls have silicone centers.

The secret of this freak silicone is that it is really an extremely slow-moving liquid. Leave a ball of it alone, and the ball slowly flattens like a pancake. Pull it apart slowly and the material flows with your pull. Pull it quickly, throw it on the floor, or hit it with a hammer, however, and it snaps, rebounds, or shatters. The molecules of bouncing putty just can't flow past each other at greater than a given speed.

If you want to see for yourself how this amazing substance works, you can now buy it under various trade names in the novelty departments of stationery, drug, cigar, and department stores.

Smoke from Empty Glasses

On the stage and in the movies white smoke is often produced by combining the invisible vapors of two common chemicals. You can conjure up similar smoke in this baffling table stunt.

Place two seemingly empty glasses mouth to mouth and cover them with a napkin. Now blow smoke from a cigarette or a piece of lighted paper toward the glasses, with the announcement that you will cause the smoke to enter them. Remove the napkin a moment later and smoke billows forth!

The secret? First secretly moisten the inside of one glass with several drops of ammonia water, and the other with several drops of hydrochloric acid. When the glasses are brought together, the vapors of the liquids combine to form white ammonium chloride.

154

Electrolysis Speeds Up Corrosion

A thin coating of tin does a splendid job in protecting from corrosion the iron of "tin cans" and other moderately used household
"tinware." Water pipes, hinges, clothesline pulleys, and other iron
objects which must stand up against the weather and rough treatment, however, are usually *galvanized,* or coated with zinc. How
can iron plated with zinc take more abuse than iron plated with
tin?

An easy experiment will give you a clue. Just make a few
scratches through the tin coating of a can and also through the
zinc coating of a clothesline pulley or other piece of galvanized ware
(left photo, above), and then leave the two objects in a damp
place for several days. At the end of that time you should see a
surprising difference. The exposed iron on the tin can will have
corroded badly—more so than if it had been ordinary uncoated
iron. On the other hand, the exposed iron on the galvanized object
will not have corroded at all; it will have been protected by a film
of corroded zinc (right photo, above).

The reason? When two different metals are in contact in the
presence of moisture, an electrochemical effect is set up which
preserves the less active metal and causes the more active one to
corrode faster than usual. As tin is *less* active than iron, a break in
tin plate speeds up the corrosion of the *iron.* As zinc is *more* active
than iron, a break in galvanized plate causes the *zinc* to corrode. In
corroding, the zinc forms over the damaged surface a tough
"skin" of oxide which stops further corrosion.

How Fire-resisting Paints Work

Although it is impossible to make wood completely unburnable it can be made nearly so by chemical treatment. The most effective way is to force a fireproofing solution under pressure into the pores of the wood; the next best is to coat it with fire-resisting paint. All cold-water paints, flat paints, and some linseed-oil paints which contain borax in place of part of the pigment have fire-retarding qualities. Many of these special paints owe this ability to sodium silicate solution (water glass).

You can show graphically how water glass works by painting a strip of wood with three coats of the solution, allowing each coat to dry before applying the next. When the last coat is dry, hold the stick over the flame of a gas range. The coating swells to a frothy mass, as shown above, which insulates the wood from the heat.

Extinguishing Fire with Foam

To put out big oil and gasoline fires in the open air, where heat and wind would drive away free carbon dioxide, this gas is applied as a blanket of thick, stable foam. The foam is prepared on the spot by mixing a solution of aluminum sulfate with another of sodium bicarbonate which contains a small amount of a foaming agent, such as licorice. You can repeat the process with chemicals found in your own kitchen. Fill two glasses each one-quarter full of water. To the first add a teaspoonful of baking soda and a pinch of powdered gelatine. To the second add a teaspoonful of powdered alum. Stir both until dissolved and pour the solutions simultaneously into a third glass. Immediately a thick white foam of carbon dioxide puffs up—finally to overflow the glass!

CHAMELEON CHEMISTRY

Water to Wine and Wine to Water

Presto-chango color transformations are everyday matters to the chemist. He mixes together colorless substances, subjects them to proper temperatures and promoters, and ends up with an array of dyes, pigments, and other chemicals that rivals the rainbow!

To him, changing "water to wine" and "wine to water" is routine business. To test the strength of a water-white solution of alkali, the chemist first adds several drops of an *indicator*, which turns it red. Then he adds an acid. As soon as the alkali is neutralized by the acid, the red solution turns white again!

Most of the "water to wine" tricks popular with the chemical magician are based on this simple acid-alkali color reaction. Here is a variation which may amaze even your amateur chemist friends.

Household ammonia will serve as the alkali and vinegar as the acid. Make up the indicator (or have your druggist do it) by dissolving 1 gram of phenolphthalein in 50 milliliters of ethyl alcohol, and then adding an equal amount of water. For equipment, you need four small glasses and an opaque or dark glass pitcher.

Secretly prepare the glasses before your demonstration. Put 10 drops of the indicator into the first and third glass, nothing into the second, and 15 drops of vinegar into the fourth. Mix 3 drops of ammonia in 12 ounces of water in the pitcher.

To perform your stunt, first pour the clear liquid from the pitcher into each of the glasses. In the first glass it turns into "wine," in the second it remains "water," in the third it becomes "wine," in the fourth it stays "water."

Pretending surprise, pour back the contents of the first three glasses into the pitcher; then repour the liquid into the glasses. This time the liquid in all three is "wine." Still surprised, pour back the contents of all four glasses. When you pour from the pitcher once again, all the glasses fill with "water"!

"Wine" and "water" appear alternately from a pitcher of "water."

Pour back and repour the first three glasses; they become "wine."

Pour back and repour all four glasses; the liquid is now "water"!

Ammonia Makes This Maiden Blush

You can make your favorite pin-up blush or pale at your will—as the young man above is trying to do—provided, of course, you have also a smattering of chemical know-how.

This amusing trick again makes use of the ability of phenolphthalein to indicate the presence of an alkali. First paint the cheeks of the portrait with a solution of phenolphthalein in alcohol and water, and allow the picture to dry. Immediately before demonstrating the stunt, moisten the cheeks slightly by dampening the back of the print. Then hold in readiness a finger you have secretly wet with household ammonia.

To make the lady blush, hold your ammonia-dampened finger near and below her face. The cheeks flush as the ammonia vapor combines with the indicator; they pale when the fumes are removed.

Red Cabbage Turns Green

Have you ever wondered why red cabbage is *purple* when cooked in plain water, *red* when pickled in vinegar, and *blue*—or even *green* —when cooked in water containing baking soda? It's because the coloring matter in red cabbage, like that in many other vegetables and fruits, is a natural indicator.

Red cabbage, beets, purple plums, and blue grapes all contain pigments called *anthocyanins*. Oddly enough, the color of plants containing these substances depends more upon the acidity or alkalinity of the sap or the processing solution than upon the particular pigments. In acid solutions their color tends to be red, in alkaline solutions, blue, while intermediate solutions make purples.

With a little red-cabbage juice (diluted with an equal amount of water), plus vinegar and ammonia, you can show these magic changes. First add several drops of vinegar; this will turn the juice red. Then add the ammonia, drop by drop, while stirring. As the acidity is neutralized, the juice becomes purple. Then it changes to blue. If more ammonia is added, an extra yellow pigment is conjured up which combines with the blue to form dark green!

Root Beer Changes to Water

Sooner or later you will meet the high-pressure salesman of some "magic" cleaning preparation, who invariably winds up his harangue by removing huge smears of iodine—"which every housewife knows is the most difficult of all stains to remove!"

As a matter of fact, iodine is one of the easiest of all stains to get rid of. Merely swab the stain with a solution of ordinary photographer's "hypo" (sodium thiosulfate) in water and the iodine is instantly changed into a colorless compound which can readily be rinsed out with plain water.

This reaction can be impressed on your friends by means of the neat stunt shown in the photographs above. You change "root beer" to "water" without opening the bottle!

Neither beverage, of course, is the real stuff. The "root beer" (poison: don't try to drink it!) is water colored with tincture of iodine. A few crystals of hypo are fastened to the under side of the bottle cap with a drop of glue or rubber cement.

To work your magic, merely give the bottle several shakes. As soon as the hypo dissolves, the liquid becomes colorless.

Ink for People Who Change Their Minds

Have you ever written something into a letter which you wished you hadn't? Here is an "ink" which you can get rid of instantly in case you don't like what you've written. Just give it a swish with a cloth and it's gone! However, it is quite useless except to astonish unsophisticated friends.

To make this ink just add a dozen drops of tincture of iodine to 3 teaspoonfuls of water, and then stir in a teaspoonful of cornstarch. The iodine reacts with the starch to form a deep blue-black coloration, a reaction which forms the standard test for the presence of starch.

Write with a clean pen. Although this ink stands out distinctly, the starch keeps it from penetrating the paper. As soon as it is dry it can be removed with the above-mentioned swish.

Water to Ink!

Most chemical color changes occur at the instant two substances are mixed. This baffling change—due to a series of complex chemical reactions which first must take place—occurs at some predetermined time seconds or minutes later. By careful timing, you can make the startling transformation seem to occur at your command.

Dissolve ½ teaspoon of potassium iodate (not io*dide*) in 32 ounces of water. Make a second solution by stirring ¼ teaspoon of sodium sulfite and ⅛ teaspoon of cornstarch in 8 ounces of boiling water; add cold water to make 32 ounces. When cool, and while stirring, add 20 drops of concentrated sulfuric acid. (More acid will speed up the reaction; less will slow it down.) At first milky, this solution will clear as excess starch settles.

To work your magic, put some of the first solution into a large tumbler or beaker and, stirring constantly, add an equal amount of the second. Then announce that you will change this "water" to "ink." At the right moment (determined by previous trial), say the magic word and, presto! the clear solution changes to midnight blue!

Pour Red, White, and Blue

As a patriotic finale to a demonstration of science magic, what could be more appropriate than to pour a colorless liquid into three glasses and have it change in the first to *red*, in the second to *white*, and in the third to *blue!* (Incidentally, these colors represent the flag not only to Americans, but to the citizens of at least a dozen other countries!)

By keeping the necessary solutions in four 1-ounce dropping bottles, you can always have this stunt handy. Number the bottles 1 to 4. In No. 1 put ¼ ounce of potassium thiocyanate; in No. 2, ¼ ounce of silver nitrate (careful, poison!); in No. 3, ¼ ounce of potassium ferrocyanide; in No. 4, ¼ ounce of ferric chloride. Fill each bottle with water and shake it to dissolve the chemical.

Before your performance, line up three glasses and secretly put 7 drops of No. 1 in the first, 7 drops of No. 2 in the second, and 2 drops of No. 3 in the third. Then put 3 glass of water into a pitcher and add 30 drops of No. 4.

When all is ready, just pour the liquid from the pitcher into the glasses, in the order named. The clear liquid changes in successive glasses to wine red, milky white, and Prussian blue!

The red and the blue color changes are both familiar to the chemist as a test for ferric iron; the change to white is a common test for chemicals containing either silver or a chloride.

166

A Color Change Indicates Humidity

Artificial flowers and dolls' dresses, impregnated with a chemical that changes color with the humidity, have long been used to indicate the relative dryness of the air. Today, moisture-absorbing agents treated with the same chemical are packed in salt-shaker caps and canister tops to keep salt and cookies dry. When these agents get too damp, the chemical notifies you by changing color.

The secret of all these devices is cobalt chloride, a chemical whose crystals lose water and turn blue when they are perfectly dry, and combine with water and turn pink when they are moist.

Cobalt chloride is an old friend of the chemical magician. To make drawings or writing which you can cause to appear or disappear at will, just draw or write with a very dilute solution of cobalt chloride in water. When first applied, this "magic ink" is such a pale pink it is practically invisible (above, left). Hold the paper over a stove, or near an electric lamp, however, and the drawing or writing comes out a bright blue (above, right). If you then breathe on the paper, the image once more disappears!

A handkerchief soaked in the same dilute solution, and then allowed to dry, can be made to change color similarly. Warm it, and it becomes bright blue; breathe on it, and it becomes pale pink, or colorless!

SCIENTIFIC SLEUTHING

How Chemistry Helps Catch Criminals

Although lone masterminds of crime detection still flourish in detective stories, most crimes of today are solved by anonymous experts in up-to-the-minute laboratories. Armed with microscopes, spectroscopes, chemical reagents, and invisible light, these scientific sleuths, working with the FBI, Army and Navy Intelligence, and state and municipal police departments, are continually outwitting even the smartest of criminals.

Some tricks used by the chemical detectives are so delicate that they require a microscope and an analytical balance, but there are many interesting tests which may be duplicated with simple chemicals and equipment in your own kitchen.

Fingerprints, one of the commonest means of identification, are transferred to objects by the fats, fatty acids, and salts exuded through the pores of the fingers. If the prints are on paper, you can usually make them visible with iodine vapor.

Put a dozen drops of tincture of iodine into a porcelain evaporating dish (a tin jar cover will do) and place the dish over low heat on an electric or gas stove. When the iodine boils, hold a piece of paper with a fingerprint on it, print side down, several inches above the dish. The print should become brown.

By another simple test, chemists often can tell if a document has been altered. Most common inks contain a tannate of iron. On exposure to air, this tannate slowly oxidizes, and in so doing forms a new tannate which resists solution in water or weak acids.

By virtue of this chemical change, it is easy to tell whether such an ink is new or relatively old. Merely apply a drop of a 5 per cent solution of oxalic acid to the questioned document. If the ink is fresh, the color will quickly run. As its age increases, the tendency to run will diminish. The color of iron tannate ink which is more than six years old should not run at all.

Held over iodine vapor, a fingerprint on paper turns dark brown.

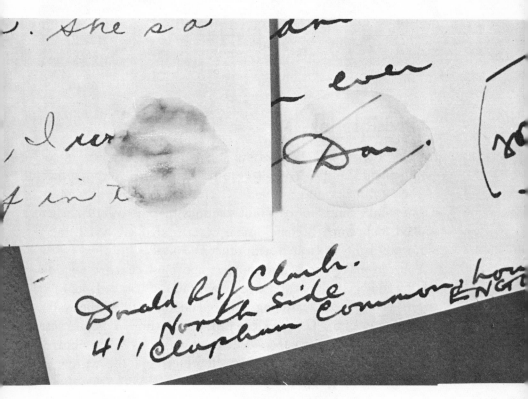

Treated with dilute acid, new ink usually runs, old ink doesn't.

Invisible Inks

Invisible or *sympathetic* inks are still important weapons of the criminal and the spy. You also can use them in performing feats of chemical magic and for writing secret letters to your friends.

These inks consist of chemical solutions that are colorless when applied, but which become visible when heated, observed under ultraviolet light, or treated with other chemicals.

You can make one of the simplest and most effective invisible inks by adding 10 drops of concentrated sulfuric acid to 1 ounce of water. (To prevent spattering, always add the acid to the water, and not vice versa.) Using a clean pen, write or draw a picture with this "ink" on ordinary paper. When the writing is dry, nothing is visible. Hold the paper over heat, however, and the writing or drawing magically appears.

170

Other common invisible inks, each with its method of development and final color, are listed in the table below.

If you have the use of a home or school laboratory, you can compound a universal developer that will make almost any secret writing visible. Dissolve 4 grams of potassium iodide, $\frac{1}{10}$ gram of iodine, 5 grams of sodium chloride, 4 grams of aluminum chloride crystals (do not use anhydrous aluminum chloride), and 3 milliliters of glycerine in 50 milliliters of water. Apply this sparingly to the paper with a wad of cotton, as shown in the photograph above.

SYMPATHETIC (INVISIBLE) INKS		
Ink	Developer	Color
sulfuric acid	heat	black
nitric acid	heat	black
cobalt chloride	gentle heat	blue
copper nitrate	potassium ferrocyanide	brown
oxalic acid	cobalt nitrate	blue
potassium thiocyanate	ferric chloride	red

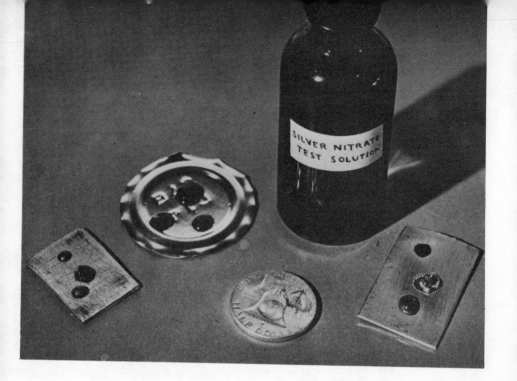

Is the Coin Counterfeit?

Have you a "silver" coin which you suspect is counterfeit? A little scientific investigation may help you find out.

Drop it on a hard surface. Genuine coins have a bell-like ring. Because they usually contain lead, most counterfeits sound dull.

Feel the coin. Lead in its composition will make it feel greasy.

Look at the corrugations around its edge. Those around good coins are even. Those around counterfeits are uneven.

Try to cut the edge with a penknife. Most counterfeits can be easily cut. Genuine coins cannot.

If none of these tests convince you, then try the acid test suggested by the U.S. Secret Service. All you need is a solution of 10 grains of silver nitrate and 20 drops of concentrated nitric acid in 1 ounce of distilled water. You can have this put up by your druggist if you haven't the facilities.

To make the test, scrape a small spot on the coin to clean it and apply a drop of the solution. If the coin is good, the acid will not change its appearance. If it is counterfeit, the acid will blacken the metal, just as it has blackened the pieces of lead, tin, and zinc shown with the genuine coin in the photograph above.

172

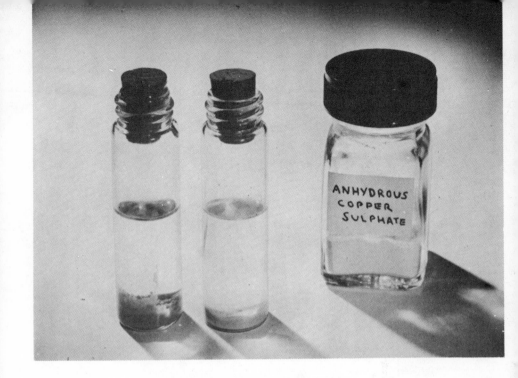

Are You Buying Water?

When you buy gasoline do you get 100 per cent "gas," or does an unscrupulous dealer mix in a little water for bad measure? With the help of a telltale powder, you can find out in an instant.

Although you probably can't buy the required powder locally, you can make some in a few minutes from ordinary copper sulfate crystals obtainable at the drugstore. Put an ounce of these blue crystals into a small glass baking dish and place the dish in an oven heated to about 490 degrees Fahrenheit. The heat dehydrates the crystals. When all the water has gone, what remains is anhydrous (waterless) copper sulfate—a pale gray powder. When the powder has cooled, bottle it for use as needed.

To make a test, put a little of your powder into a small vial and add some of the suspected gasoline. Then stopper the vial and give it a few shakes. If the gas contains water, the copper sulfate will take back what it lost and turn blue, as in the left-hand vial shown above. If the gas is water-free, the powder will remain gray, as in the right-hand vial.

You can also use this test to detect water in absolute alcohol, or in any other liquid that ordinarily does not contain it.

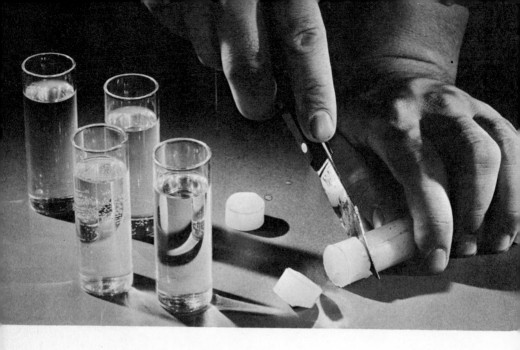

Test Your Antifreeze

According to car experts, only two types of antifreeze can safely be used in present-day automobiles. One is the "temporary" type, which consists usually of ethyl or methyl alcohol. The other is the "permanent" type, usually ethylene glycol. Antifreeze containing salts or petroleum is completely unacceptable.

Luckily—even if the maker's label doesn't tell you—you can find out if your new antifreeze is of the dangerous or safe variety by means of a little scientific detective work.

Relative weight gives the first clue. Pour a sample of undiluted antifreeze into a small vial, and drop into it a slice from a paraffin candle. If the slice floats, the antifreeze is of either the glycol or the salt-base type. If it sinks, the antifreeze is either alcohol or petroleum.

To tell glycol from salt-base antifreeze, heat a small sample in a jar cover until the liquid has completely boiled away. Glycol leaves little or no residue, while salt-base antifreeze leaves a heap of white to brownish crystals.

Finally, to distinguish alcohol from petroleum, light several drops on a bit of cotton. Alcohol burns with a clear, blue flame; petroleum with a yellow, smoky one.

174

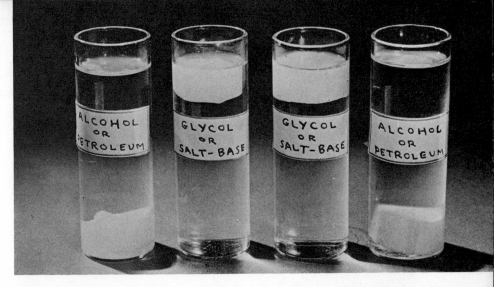

This simple sink-float test helps tell what your antifreeze is.

Glycol or salt-base? The amount of residue after boiling is a clue.

Alcohol or petroleum? You can tell by the character of the flame.

What Plastic Is That?

Is that glasslike rod you just bought made of acrylate or of styrene plastic? Is that new shirt made of nylon, rayon (cellulose), or acetate (cellulose acetate)? Are those plastic drinking cups made of styrene (which melts in boiling water) or of urea or melamine (which don't melt)?

You can easily tell the difference between these and half a dozen other common plastics with nothing but a match, a pair of tweezers, your eyes, your nose, and the chart on the facing page.

To make a test, cut or shave off a small piece of the plastic. Holding it in tweezers, let it barely touch the match flame. If it doesn't catch fire, hold it there for not more than 10 seconds. Note the color it gives to the flame. If it does burn, note its own flame color. After 10 seconds, blow the flame out, smell the fumes given off by the smoldering plastic, and try to match the flame color and the odor with those listed on the chart.

176

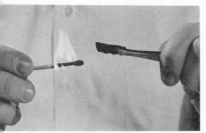

No flame. The sample retains its shape. Note its smell.

Color and Nature of Flame	Odor of Smoldering Plastic	Type of Plastic
	formaldehyde	UREA
	formaldehyde plus fishlike odor	MELAMINE
	formaldehyde plus carbolic acid	PHENOLIC

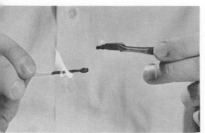

Sample burns but goes out away from flame. Return it to edge of flame, note color it imparts.

pronounced green area in flame	burnt rubber	PLIOFILM
small green area with much yellow	burnt rubber	NEOPRENE
green area	acrid but not burnt rubber	VINYL
green area	sweet	VINYLIDINE
green; sparks from burning plastic	vinegar	ACETATE

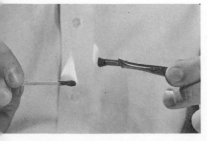

Sample keeps on burning after removal from flame. Judge flame color during the first second.

When making tests, don't blow out the match along with the plastic, or the match smell will confuse you. If possible, test some known samples before tackling unknown ones.

intense white; burns fiercely		NITRATE
mostly blue, white tip	floral, fruity odor	ACRYLATE
blue	burning leaves or fresh celery	NYLON
yellowish, bright green mantle	burnt rubber	PLIOFILM
yellow-white luminous; smoky	sweet floral	STYRENE
yellow-white luminous	burnt paper	CELLULOSE
weak; small green mantle, much yellow	burnt rubber	NEOPRENE
yellow-green mantle	vinegar	ACETATE
yellow-green mantle; burns well, once started	slight, sweet	ETHYL CELLULOSE

Index

179

180

181